ABOUT YOGA

ABOUT YOGA

THE COMPLETE PHILOSOPHY

HARVEY DAY

THORSONS PUBLISHERS LTD
91 ST MARTIN'S LANE, LONDON, W C 2

First published 1951
Second Edition 1951

MADE AND PRINTED IN GREAT BRITAIN BY
MORRISON AND GIBB LIMITED, LONDON AND EDINBURGH

CONTENTS

CHAPTER I

An Introduction to Yoga. Some Yoga Miracles

LET me explain that this is not a text book on Yoga, and that when you have read the last page of the book, you will not be a compleat Yogi. If I promised to make you a yogi I should be taking your money under false pretences. The Yoga philosophy is much too vast to be contained in so slim a volume, or for that matter in any single volume. Yoga cannot be mastered by reading books or following written instructions. It can be mastered only by long and arduous practise.

If you want to be a yogi I know of only one way to do so. Take ship to India, seek out a *guru* or master and serve your apprenticeship under his guidance. And where is such a master to be found? I cannot say, because I don't know. Yogis seldom have a fixed abode. They have no possessions to tie them to one spot. And yogis who are masters of their cult are few and far between. You may have to seek far and wide, and then you may not find him. Even if you do, he may reject you, for you must first prove the genuineness of your desire.

You will want to know, then, why I am wasting your time, and what this book is all about. What is it that I am trying to say?

If to be a compleat yogi is impossible in Britain, to gain some knowledge of Yoga, both practical as well as theoretical, is not. A good deal of yoga can be adapted to suit a civilised way of living, and if practised regularly will clear your mind, increase your powers of concentration and determination, help you to overcome worry, and eradicate fear.

It will also make you fit, mentally and physically. A good many yoga teachings can be carried out, no matter how old you are. Yoga poses can be done with considerable benefit by the young, as well as by the aged; but it is the aged who will derive more benefit from yoga than the young. Young people are impatient. They want results —quickly. And yoga is a science that you can't just pep up. It isn't like an Army course. You can't jam three years work into six weeks.

In the final stages of the war I was attached, as a civilian, to an Army Education School in Warwickshire where the military authorities allowed me to instruct as I wanted. It was an exhilarating experience. But unfortunately the length of each course was determined by the War Office. The Pundits, for whom I have, of course, enormous respect, used to send out orders: " You will run a course lasting one month, on English Literature, from Chaucer to the present day." Or, " You will run a 17-day course called Man and Society, embracing Man's development from Pre-historic times."

History and English, and many another subject may be taken by the Army in tabloid form—but not Yoga. Results from yoga depend entirely upon the time given to it, and upon the state of your mind when practising it. And the state of your mind often depends upon your physical condition. " There was never yet philosopher," says Shakespeare, " could endure the tooth-ache patiently."

Yoga is not easy to master. If it were, any nincompoop could be a yogi.

I am not a yogi. I make no claims to miraculous or even unusual powers. But, by the constant practise of certain mental, physical and spiritual exercises, adapted to suit my western way of living, I keep in good health, and as each year rolls on *I feel fitter and stronger and more full of energy than before*. I can think more lucidly, and my faculties are more alert than they were twenty years ago. I have no fears, and I refuse to worry. I have now reached the state when I am trying to make myself immune from heat and cold. Excessive cold I dislike. It makes me uncomfortable and when I can ignore the weather utterly, I shall be much happier physically.

Is all this worth while? I think it is. I value health, for if one is healthy one does not need to think about the body. I know, because I have ailed for many years. I was born in the malarial swamps of India. My life was despaired of a few days after birth, and my well meaning parents, in their ignorance of such matters, sent out an S.O.S. for a priest from a town 150 miles distant, in order that I might be baptised. I confess that the act made little difference to my soul. That is, if I possess a soul in the conventional sense.

For the first fifteen years hardly a week went by without a bout of malaria, ague or dengue. If I rose free of fever and lay down the same night without a rise in temperature, I felt that the gods had worked a minor miracle.

Nor was it that I lacked either food, care or sunshine. I ate of the " best and richest," which I now know to be faulty feeding. Ever since I can remember I had a servant who devoted his entire energies to carrying out my selfish whims. More sun poured down on my miserable, sickly carcase each week than one gets in England during an entire summer. Even so, my parents spent a small fortune in doctors' bills and patent medicines; tonics and fattening foods.

It would be pleasant to record that I embraced yoga and in a flash rid myself of all my ailments. But I did nothing of the sort. I saw and spoke with many yogis and fakirs. They visited my father and discussed the various Indian holy books with him. They wasted hours in metaphysical discussions. My mother gave them food and alms, but I regarded most of them as feckless, irresponsible, lazy people who battened on the poor, incredulous natives. And so they were—or most of them.

Most of the yogis and fakirs one comes across in India are charlatans; if not wholly so, at any rate partly.

My ambition was to be healthy. Because I was always ill, I valued fitness and strength more than anything in the world.

I first tasted health when I was sent to a school where they let me play hockey and football bare-footed, a state my parents had always been warned against. "Don't let him run about without boots," the doctors used to warn my mother, "or he'll get hookworm, or a chill in his bladder." Needless to say, I've had neither.

"Put your hat on," my father used to admonish, "or you'll get sunstroke." But at this strange new school I played hockey hatless under a brassy mid-day sun for hours every high day and holiday, and grew more healthy for it.

School meals consisted of rough, coarse food, which to my pampered palate was at first unappetising. It consisted mainly of vegetables, for we were given meat only once a week, and that as a treat. Hunger and hard exercise gave me the appetite I had hitherto lacked.

I slept on an iron sheet on which there was no mattress. All that separated my body from the iron was a cotton " durrie," about as thick as tent canvas. My pillow was stuffed with coir, and soon became lumpy. I doubt if I slept more than a few minutes the first few nights, for it was impossible to gain any comfort on that hard, unyielding surface; but in less than a fortnight I was sleeping as never before, and eventually, when I went home for holidays, I found a feather mattress intolerably stuffy. It so nearly suffocated me that I used to get out and sleep on the carpet.

Each morning we were awakened at six and led bare-footed across grassy playing fields thick with dew, to a bath house, where we plunged into icy water. In summer it was a pleasure; in winter a penance.

Then followed a period of physical exercise and breakfast followed that. It consisted of two large cups of tea and a roll. When I bit into my roll the first morning I closed my teeth on a marble that had been inserted skilfully inside it, and as I took it out of my mouth in alarm and disgust, everyone roared with laughter. Later, I thought it quite funny when played on other new boys—such was our schoolboy sense of fun.

I remember one young chap, nicknamed " Gobbie," because of his immense mouth, who used to devour his roll at a single mouthful. It was, as the Irish so picturesquely put it, " no more than a daisy in the mouth of a bull." One morning, from a perverted sense of fun, some humorist placed a taw (large marble) in his roll. Gobbie swallowed the lot without fuss, apparently ignorant of the fact that a taw had been inserted in his; but he was none the worse, for he played a leading part that afternoon in winning a match for his house.

My first recollection of school was that of a boy much bigger and stronger than I, who approached and asked truculently whether I could fight him. Without considering the consequences, I said I thought so, and the next instant found myself lying on my back in a flower bed, not knowing exactly how I got there. I rose and squared up to him and was promptly knocked down again and again because I was too ignorant to give the conventional sign of surrender. Eventually someone stopped the massacre and I was led away.

That should have finished me; but it was merely the beginning.

Though still weak enough to feel tremendously fatigued when I ran once round the playing field, I improved in health. I first spent many weeks, and then days in the school sanitorium; but the next year they were fewer, and the following year fewer still. In my last year I did not even go near the place.

If ever you've been as ill as I was, you will know that my all-consuming desire was for health. How I envied those who were never ill! What would I have done to change places with them?

Because I had been an invalid for so many years, I grew to love books. Through the written pages I could roam the world as I lay in bed. My pocket money was limited by a school rule to fivepence a week, and when I had devoured the two books a week we were allowed from the school library, I would slip over the school wall and visit secondhand bookshops in the town. Often I had the equivalent of only a penny or twopence, but secondhand books were cheap, and those I had read could be exchanged. I grew so to love raking round secondhand bookshops that to-day it is only by the greatest exercise of will that I can pass one. I have always found them far more intriguing than the shops that sell new books.

It was in these old shops in the fascinating but dirty city of Calcutta that I discovered treasure trove: books on adventure, sport, romance; books about strong men; books about health and diet; books on philosophy, religion, Yoga—books on every subject under the sun. What they thought of me in Mr. Audy's shop in College Street I shall never know; for I was always there, buying and exchanging, and reading on the spot the books I could not afford to take away.

Books on health interested me vastly—and those on strength. How I envied those wonderful people—Mr. Earle Liedermann, Mr. Jowett and others, who assured me that they could literally cover my puny body with muscle in the short space of seven days. My friends and I used to write to them in America—they invited us to do so!— and they mailed us expensively printed mouth-watering brochures setting forth their claims, backed by impressive testimonials. The booklets were profusely illustrated with pictures of their pupils, all of whom seemed to be supermen positively bulging with muscles I did not realise even existed.

These specimens I now regard as grotesque.

But alas, on fivepence a week I was never able to put Mr. Liederman n to the test. Mr. Jowett will never be able to point his finger at me and exclaim, " I made you a champ!" It wasn't for want of inducement. When I failed to reply to their letters, both Mr. Liedermann and Mr. Jowett showered me with handsome offers, reducing their rates by dollars, offering me free cheques if I would sign on within ten days, and calling me *friend, comrade* and even *brother*. I felt positively ashamed at having treated them so churlishly, and if this book should ever fall into their hands, I trust they will realise that my apology is as handsome as their offers were.

But if the wonderfully complicated apparatus of Mr. Liedermann and the massive dumb bells of Mr. Jowett were denied me, I could at least breathe.

They told me at school that deep breathing was good for one; so I breathed as deeply and as often as I could. Later, some of the first breathing exercises I performed were based on Yoga. One of the first stomach exercises I mastered was the yoga *Uddiyana Bandha*. I have done it before my bath for more than thirty years.

I read some of the books printed by Bernarr MacFadden and did some of his exercises, and though I did not know it then, some of these were based on yoga breathing and yoga postures. Later, when I left school and met and conversed with yogis, they taught me more about such things. In one old book by MacFadden that I bought at school was an exercise for the spine, which was based on the posture known as *ardhamatsyendrasana*.

How fortunate I was to have only fivepence a week pocket money; otherwise Mr. Liedermann or Mr. Jowett would have got me.

My first contacts with yogis came at an early age. My father, a jute merchant who grew and pressed his own fibre before dispatching it to the mills, employed a great many people. When they were in trouble he helped them;

when they were ill, he and my mother ministered to them. There were few doctors in that part of India, and my parents doctored hundreds suffering with cholera, dysentry, typhoid and plague.

It was a snake-infested country and there must have been dozens of snakes in the house, and hundreds in the grounds. Often in the morning we found shed skins, and sometimes snakes even slithered past us. But none of us was ever bitten. Seldom a month passed, however, without someone in our employ being bitten, and I have witnessed scores of coolies die of snake-bite.

One afternoon when I was about ten I remember a great commotion in the garden. A crowd had gathered, as crowds do in the East, babbling and jabbering away without doing very much. My mother was summoned and told that a *mali* (gardener) had been bitten by a cobra. He lay in agony. We had no snake-bite serum; in fact, in more than twenty years in India I never saw an outfit containing snake-bite serum. In spite of the fact that more than 300 people died *every day* of snake-bite, I don't think the government instituted research on any but the smallest scale. Native labour was cheap, and when a dozen died, two dozen others were ready to step into their shoes.

My mother was a most practical person. She was about to slash the wound, rub in grains of permanganate of potash, fasten a tourniquet and dose the man with whisky when a yogi, whom we knew, pushed his way through the crowd and took charge of the situation.

" Leave him to me;" he turned to my mother, " he will be all right." The crowd stood back, the yogi tied some string about the man's limb, muttered a *mantra* or two (incantations) and applied *phoonk* (breath). Soon the victim's breathing became easier, the pain he complained of vanished, and in a few hours he was normal, when in fact he should have been dead.

The yogi, to whom my mother often gave food, would accept no reward, and went his way. Nor did we ever see him again.

I had seen similar *miracles* before—and since.

I knew that yogis and fakirs had powers beyond those of ordinary men. My *ayah* (nurse) and my personal servant often told me, in order to frighten me, that they were wicked men who would take me away if I were disobedient, and all through my early childhood I was frightened by *bhooths, patenebooris* (djins) and wild animals. I was also told that the *aghas* (Kabulis; tall, massive men wearing bushy beards and baggy pantaloons) would whisk me away in the big bags they carried if I were naughty. In India there are many more things to curdle a child's blood than in Britain. Many a night I lay awake listening to the blood-curdling wails of jackals, and the weird cries of hyenas, which I was told simulated the cries of children. And when the door was opened they rushed in and snatched babies away in their powerful jaws.

From my very earliest days I never doubted that yogis and fakirs possessed powers that ordinary mortals did not, but I was also convinced that most of them used their powers for evil. And I am afraid that a great many of them do.

Not all yogis; not even the majority of yogis can perform so-called miracles. But a great many have acquired just so much skill that they can perform some pet feat with which to impress the multitude. And in India the multitude is ignorant, superstitious and easily impressed. And these *fakers* extract money and food from the poor, and live in comparative ease and leisure.

But the men who have mastered yoga—and they may be counted on the fingers of one hand—care nothing for such tricks and devices. Later I shall enlarge on the cult of Yoga, the different forms there are, and what each sets out to achieve. By that time you may decide that Yoga is much too difficult an art to master. You will be right, for not one in a hundred million masters the art completely.

But there are many who master some branch of Yoga and are the better for it. They cannot work miracles, unless perfect health, complete freedom from worry, and the ability to think clearly can be termed miracles. And from what I see of people around me, they are minor miracles.

That which is worth doing is never easy. The more worthwhile it is, the more difficult. It is not really difficult to grow rich if you are willing to pinch and scrape and bury your scruples. That is why there are so many who pay super tax. But to be really happy—which has nothing to do with money—is an exceedingly difficult art. And that is why there are so few really happy people.

If you don't believe me, think of the perfectly happy people you know, and it will surprise you how few there are.

If some person tells you that any goal is easy to achieve; remember that either the goal is not worth reaching, or the person is—perhaps inadvertently—deceiving you and himself.

Why, to become a proficient golfer, which is merely a matter of striking a little ball with a club-headed stick so that it lodges in a hole in the ground—is a simple operation that drives strong men into a frenzy, makes them lose control of themselves and fills them with eloquence. And any man who can wield this stick in such a manner that he can knock the little white ball into a hole in the ground is rewarded with cups, medals, the adulation of millions, and an income a prince may well envy. Fully grown business men and others with responsibilities have been known to desert their wives and families for entire days at a stretch, to achieve a measure of success at this somewhat futile pastime.

Millions die without knocking the little ball into the little hole as many times as they would like.

If this mere mechanical operation, this somewhat debased form of manual labour, which has neither dignity nor purpose, is so difficult to master, how much more so a complete philosophy like Yoga?

Men and women—for there are women yogins—set out with the best will in the world to master this cult; but most of them fall by the wayside. Miracles are not achieved easily, otherwise they would no longer be miracles. When they are three-a-penny, no one will want to perform them.

The yogi says that nothing is a miracle and that any man can achieve what he sets out to do. By *miracle* we mean some feat that defies natural laws, such, for instance, as levitation. For a man so to defy gravity as to raise himself so that his body is suspended in mid-air, is, civilised Man would say, a miracle. Yet my friend Swami Shri Purhoit has, I believe, performed this feat many times before reliable witnesses, and he has never claimed full yogic powers. Dr. Alexander Cannon, Ph.D.,

18

F.R.C.S., M.D., etc., etc., Psychiatrist and research worker at a mental hospital at Colney Hatch, claims to have levitated himself across a gorge in the Himalayas. In his book, *Invisible Influence,* he says that while journeying in Tibet his party came to a wide gorge 300 feet deep, through which flowed a swift, impassable river. One of the party was a Tibetan sage, who decided that they would cross by means of levitation.

Dr. Cannon writes: " He gave us instructions as to how we should cross this gulf by practising the levitation and transportation formula in which we had become ere this, adept in its perfect manipulation.

" Within the course of a few hours we made our bodily state fit to allow of this great miraculous transportation phenomenon taking place by pure mental effort, and in another moment of time we were both landed safely on the other side."

When Dr. Cannon returned to London and wrote a book about his experiences he was dismissed by the L.C.C. They took the view that a man who could write such a book was unfit to practise in a mental hospital. In addition to possessing a long string of degrees, Dr. Cannon is a member of numerous medical and scientific societies, and is the author of a standard medical text book on psychiatry. He has been a medical officer in charge of prisons, a government pathologist, an alienist of note, a medical jurist in the High Court of Justice, and a lecturer in morbid anatomy.

So many eminent doctors and scientists wrote to the L.C.C. corroborating Dr. Cannon's statements that he was quickly reinstated.

We don't often hear of the miracles performed by yogis, because they are not professional showmen. They don't perform miracles for money or kudos. On rare occasions some of them have performed miraculous deeds, which have been witnessed by reliable persons and recorded.

Yogis have abstained from food, water *and air* for long periods; periods which no normal man could possibly survive. The oldest and best known recorded instance occurred in 1837, the details of which are set down in a little pamphlet published by Sir Claude Wade, and, I believe, preserved at the India Office.

While he was at the court of Ranjit Singh a fakir allowed himself to be buried for a period of six weeks, during which time he had neither food, water, nor air. The fakir was buried in the presence of the ruler and a Captain Osborne, as well as many lesser witnesses. His body was placed in a square building called a " *barra durra* " in the middle of one of the gardens adjoining the palace. The vault in which he lay was sealed with bricks and mortar; the door was plastered in mud and stamped with the ruler's private seal, and four sentries, relieved every two hours, were placed on four sides of the building, which was constantly inspected by officers.

At the end of six weeks Ranjit Singh broke the seal and the vault was entered.

The fakir lay in a grave some three feet below the level of the floor, in a wooden box four feet by three. This was also sealed and padlocked. When the seals were broken they beheld the figure of the fakir enclosed in a linen bag, tied at the mouth. The bag was slit, revealing the shrivelled form of the fakir, folded to fit his box.

His servant had received instructions about reviving him. This he did by bathing the stiff limbs with warm water, and restoring them to life by means of friction. A warm wheaten cake was placed on his head, and this was repeated at short intervals. Wax and cotton that had been stuffed into ears and nostrils were removed. Then, a knife was inserted with difficulty between the fakir's clenched teeth, and while holding the jaws open, his servant drew the fakir's tongue from the entrance of his throat, which it had blocked. It flew back two or three times to close the gullet, but each time was pulled forward again. His eyes were then rubbed with *ghee* (clarified butter).

Finally, the body became convulsed, the nostrils distended, the eyes resumed their natural colour and the fakir became sufficiently animated to take a deep breath and ask Ranjit Singh, " Do you believe me now?"

I have never seen a yogi or fakir buried for days and then brought back to life, but the late Mr. Harry Price told me that he had witnessed the resuscitation of a dervish in Tangier, after the man had been buried for ten or twelve days.

We talk about such feats as miracles, but the yogis don't. I have spoken with many, and they merely claim that they have discovered some secrets which the West has not yet probed. They confess that scientists in the West have discovered many that have baffled them.

No yogi, for instance, discovered how to pass an electric current from its source at the power house to a lamp many miles distant. To them that is a miracle. The secret of impinging a television picture on to a screen is another they are ignorant about. Nor can they make a car, a motor cycle or an airplane.

They merely claim that they have mastered some secrets that have hitherto eluded us, and we a great many that have baffled them.

We think telepathy wonderful, and men like Dr. Rhine, of Duke University in the United States, and Dr. Soal, of Queen Mary's College, London, spend much of their time over such things as extra-sensory perception, and whether we can see ahead into time. Such things the yogis claim to be able to do.

They claim to be able to project not only their minds into the future, but their bodies into space. They can speak to each other across hundreds of miles, and many can read your thoughts as you sit facing them. It is an uncanny and confusing experience to sit opposite a man who can tell you exactly what you are thinking, especially if you have no control whatsoever over your thoughts. For all of us think many things that we would not dream of committing to paper.

It is the physical miracles that yogis and fakirs perform that excite our imagination; and a few of them have even performed their miracles in Paris, New York and London, before audiences composed of responsible people.

In 1926 a doctor named Tarah Bey came to London and agreed to give a demonstration of his very remarkable powers. He stuck pins deeply into his flesh without causing either pain or the appearance of blood. But that is a trick that many who are not fakirs can also do.

Then he lay on a bed of nails and an anvil placed on his chest was pounded heartily by two men with sledge-hammers. This caused him no apparent discomfort, and though the feat is beyond most normal people, strong men often perform it on the music hall stage. Nor is the trick uncommon among yogis. After that he fell into a cateleptic trance, was placed in a coffin and sand was shovelled over him. He was taken out twenty minutes

22

later none the worse for his experience. Finally, as a test of mind projection, he was asked which horse would win the Derby.

"Coronach," was his reply, and sure enough, seven weeks later, Lord Woolavington's Coronach romped home.

Being locked in a coffin over which sand is shovelled is an ordeal that would tax the nerve of any normal man. The psychological effect of sealing a man in a coffin is tremendous. It gives him claustrophobia; but a yogi trained to hold his breath for long periods would find little difficulty in lasting twenty minutes. I have seen a yogi submerge himself in a lake for more than ten minutes, and many can hold their breath for half an hour or more without discomfort.

So, while we cannot dismiss Dr. Bey's exhibition as a piece of fakery, we should realise that it is not as difficult as it appears.

A series of much more difficult feats were those recorded by Sir Charles Allom some years ago. In 1928 an Indian fakir was invited to give a demonstration before a group of medical men and scientists at a London theatre. Some forty people were present, among them some of London's most distinguished physicians.

The fakir swallowed his tongue and went into a cateleptic trance. This business of going into a trance at will is a feat beyond the power of normal men, and is the result of many years of the study and practise of yoga, and is in itself a minor miracle, for in such a trance one is able either to suspend breathing or regulate it.

He was asked to regulate his pulse beat and consented to do so, and those present found that he could at will lower it to 20 a minute or raise it to 120, though the normal pulse beat is about 72. Within a few minutes he was able to accelerate his heart by 100 a minute!

Then two very sharp knife blades were placed in vices and the back of his neck was rested on one, while his ankles were placed on the other. His body remained rigid and the knife blades, which, with the weight placed on them should have cut deeply into his flesh, merely indented the skin without breaking it.

After this a large stone was placed on his stomach and assistants battered it with sledge hammers, but they might just as well have been stroking him with feathers for all the difference it made.

Now a long thin blade was pushed into his neck at one side and out through the other; and skewers were pushed through one cheek and out through the other. There were a few drops of blood, but the wounds began to heal the moment the knives and skewers were removed. Within ten minutes the flesh closed and there were no scars to show that the fakir had been subjected to such treatment.

Medical men present said that the miraculous healing was due to his pulse control, but they could not account for the fact that no scars remained. Nor could they explain why the fakir was not seriously injured by the knife that was pushed through his neck, or discomforted by the skewers through his cheeks.

A coffin was now dragged in, the fakir placed in it and his body covered with sand. When he was completely covered, the lid was screwed on and his assistant lectured the group for fifteen minutes. The lid was unscrewed, the sand shovelled away and removed from ears, nostrils and mouth, and the faker came out of his trance looking far less the worse for wear than most of us would after a ride in an excursion train to Brighton.

The fakir claimed that he could see into the future, so instantly the minds of those present switched to something of material gain. " What," they asked with one voice, " will win the Derby?" The race was a good six months off.

Apparently fakirs also seem to have a knowledge of racing lore, for instantly this gentleman replied, " Trigo," and though there were a number of racehorse owners present, and most of the others were interested in the turf, none knew the existence of such an animal. Anyway, they thought, we've tripped him, and he's sure to come a purler.

But on Derby Day Mr. Barnett's Trigo, an outsider at 33 to 1 in an unusually large field of 26, confounded the experts and proved the fakir right.

The man who has mastered yoga breathing, concentration, meditation and yoga postures eventually becomes immune to both heat and cold. Dr. Dyherenfurth, who led an expedition to the Himalayas, told an audience on his return that some Tibetans had mastered the secret of creating warmth through the power of suggestion. They had taken up the challenge of Shakespeare when he wrote:

> " O, who can hold a fire in his hand
> By thinking on the frosty Caucasus?"

All who have had dealings with yogis and fakirs in the Himalayas have seen them sit virtually naked out of doors in the coldest weather. Alexandra David-Neel gives a vivid description of their practice of *tumo*, which enables a person to generate psychic heat. *Tumo* is achieved only by long practice. She writes that her teacher told her to go to a lonely spot to bathe, and then without drying her body or putting on clothes to spend the night motionless

25

and in meditation. The altitude was 10,000 feet, and though it was not winter, the night was chilly, and she felt pleased and proud that she did not contract a chill as a result of her bodily exposure.

It requires extensive practice of exercises, breathing, meditation and concentration to achieve the perfection needed if *tumo* is to be mastered. When the neophyte is ready for his test he is taken at midnight in mid-winter, preferably when an icy wind is sweeping over the Tibetan plateau, to a frozen lake or stream. A hole is chopped in the ice and in this sits the naked neophyte. Cloths are dipped in water and wrapped round his shoulders, and he must dry them by generating heat from his body! If by daybreak he succeeds in drying three, he is given the title of *Repa* or Cotton Clad One. Dr. Dyherenfurth says that adepts can dry as many as twenty cloths in the course of a single night. Once the title of *Repa* is won, the recipient seldom wears anything but a single cotton garment, no matter how low the temperature.

For this reason alone, if for nothing else, it is worth while to practise yoga breathing, for the exercises known as *kapalabhati* and *bhastrika*, among other things, help to create bodily warmth. I claim no especial yogic powers, but all last winter, after doing these two breathing exercises, I could lie in cold water and read the four leading articles of *The Times* or the *Manchester Guardian* without experiencing the least discomfort.

This procedure can be reversed, and other breathing exercises, such as *Sitali* and *Sitkari*, tend to keep the body cool in the warmest weather. There is much more to it of course, than merely doing a few breathing exercises. One must undergo an arduous training in concentration and meditation to achieve real power. When this is completed the yoga is ready to undergo the ordeal of *panch-dhuni*—the five fires.

He sits naked in the sand in mid-summer, usually on the bank of a wide river. Huge fires are lighted to north, south, east and west of him, the fifth fire being the mid-day sun. If he can stand the ordeal not only without flinching, but with complete indifference, he is considered to be immune from extreme heat.

Such an expert can walk on glowing charcoal with impunity.

In 1931 I published an article, with photographs, in *Health and Strength* at which I described a feat by a yogi at a *mela* (fair) in India. His feet were tied to the apex of a large wooden tripod, and he hung head down. On the ground immediately below him raged a fire made from charcoal and wood. The flames played in his long hair without singeing it, and the yogi was unharmed.

I have told many people about this apparent miracle and they all replied that I must have been hypnotised, for it is impossible to come into contact with fire without being burned. Perhaps I was hypnotised—who knows? But then, the camera must have been hypnotised, too, and by means of hypnotism an impression of something non-existent must have been placed on a highly sensitive negative. If so, that too was a miracle. One can't have it both ways. I am willing, however, to listen to any reasonable explanation of what was to me a marvel.

There are cases on record of photographs being taken of yogis in the company of others, which when developed have shown all the people in the group except the yogis. Again, I can give no reason for something that is beyond me, but because I cannot readily explain it, I do not deny the possibility.

A feat is not impossible because you have not seen it done, nor is an object non-existent because you have not seen it. A fact is none the less true because you do not believe, or because the rest of the world denies that it is so.

Some yogis can eat and drink poisons without suffering ill-effect. In 1934 an astonishing demonstration was given by the Swami Narasingha at the University of Calcutta, before a body of distinguished men and professors, among them Sir C. V. Raman, 1930 winner of the Nobel Prize for his discovery of the diffusion of light, known as the *Raman effect*.

The Swami ate lethal doses of sulphuric acid, carbolic acid, and a gramme of cyanide—all without deleterious effect. Immediately after, as was the custom, he flushed his system with water; a gallon or more in one successive stream from mouth to anus. This cleared the poison from his body.

Narasingha grew careless, however, and one night, after a demonstration, he failed to carry out the cleansing processes. He had imbibed considerable quantities of *aqua regis*, broken glass and half-inch nails in addition to his usual diet of poison. He remained chatting long after his exhibition; the poison took effect, paralysis set in, and he died in hospital writhing in agony.

This, if nothing else, proves that he was not a creator of miracles, but could perform certain purely physical feats which depended upon a sufficient degree of mental and bodily development. I believe that anyone who schools himself to a sufficient mental and physical discipline, such as yogis do, can emulate their feats.

According to Surendranath Dasgupta (History of Indian Philosophy, Vol. 1—1922) several yogis proved that they could hold their breath for abnormal periods. Two known to the author (Dasgupta) were Baliknath, who at 120 years of age had the physique of a young man; and Serudnath, *who could hold his breath for two days!* Another, Sanjanath, was reputed to be seven hundred years old, but had not a single grey hair in his head. In India there was until recently no compulsory registration of births, so it was notoriously difficult to ascertain any man's age, and in this instance we may allow a certain licence. His age was told by what the yogi could recollect of people at a time when he was a boy. Obviously Dasgupta was a sincere man and a scholar, and there was, moreover, no point in setting down a story that would undoubtedly cause people to raise their eyebrows.

I knew a yogi who claimed to be well over a hundred and fifty years old, and his tale of battles and other events, and his description of uniforms and customs went a long way to verifying his story. There was no point in lying, for the man wanted neither money nor fame.

One could write almost endlessly on the feats of yogis and fakirs, dervishes, the Sungmas of Tibet who perform incredible feats of strength when possessed by demons and spirits, and other sects about which civilised people know little or nothing, but one further example should be enough to convince the sceptic that what we call miracles are sometimes performed by " ignorant savages." Some years ago Sir T. Vijayaraghavachari wrote a description in the *Hindustan Times* of a test he applied to a very remarkable yogi—a test that would certainly try the powers of most western geniuses to the limit. It called for extraordinary powers of concentration and memory. Moreover, it was carried out in public.

The yogi claimed that if a number of persons performed different operations simultaneously, he could follow them all and repeat everything that was said and done.

One man rang a bell a number of times; the number of strokes to be counted by the yogi. Another dictated a complicated mathematical problem. A third recited a long series of verses from an abstruse religious poem. A fourth set the yogi the task of compiling a poem in a specified metre. A fifth carried on a metaphysical discussion in different languages; and finally a man kept turning a spoken wheel, and the yogi was expected to count the number of revolutions it made.

Each operation required so much concentration that it seemed likely that his mind would be distracted. Each person knew exactly what he was doing, but the yogi had to focus his attention on all that was happening, and repeat accurately each operation.

I have tested my own puny capabilities by listening to a piece of poetry and at the same time watching the revolutions made by a wheel, and I have found it impossible to memorise the poem and watch the wheel simultaneously. As for counting the strokes of a bell, well . . . the mere counting of the strokes of a bell, or watching a wheel spin is enough to make most people cross-eyed and give them a headache if they have to do something else as well.

But the yogi passed his test without making a single error. And when the test was done, he departed without leaving his name, and was not seen again in the district.

The value of such a man to a commercial house could not be over-estimated. He could pass any examination with ease, and achieve any ambition he desired. But yogis have no earthly ambition. They renounce all desire either for honour, fame or possessions when once they take on the yoke.

A few yogis even claim the power of restoring the dead to life. I have often heard of such miracles, but have never seen one. F. Yeats-Brown describes a visit to Babu Bisuddhanan Dhan of Puri, who used to resuscitate sparrows and produce perfumes out of the air. And in his autobiography, Paramhansa Yogananda describes a series of even more amazing miracles.

It is easy to scoff at things one has not seen and cannot or will not believe are possible. Shakespeare admitted that "there are more things in heaven and earth than are dreamt of in our philosophy," and Pope warned against superficial learning when he wrote, "A little learning is a dangerous thing; Drink deep, or taste not the Pierian spring." If our knowledge was merely empirical, how shallow it would be. There is so much we must take on trust.

I have met people who say that all yogis are frauds and tricksters, though they have never met one, yet they will take on trust all sorts of scientific facts that they have never tried to prove. They will believe that light travels at a speed of 186,000 miles a second; that the light from some stars has been travelling for 1,500 years before reaching us; that there are more stars in the firmament than all the grains of sand on all the sea shores in this world; that the sea is six miles deep; that the middle of the earth is a liquid, molten mass; that there is a lost continent called Atlantis; that Salvador Dali is a genius; *Finnegan's Wake* is the greatest book ever written; and the United States is Democracy.

They will accept all these statements because some *authority* tells them it is so. But tell them that a yogi can levitate himself, or that one yogi can speak to another over a considerable distance, and they will want instant and conclusive proof. Such is the inconsistency of human beings. But I'm not worried whether you believe that yogis can do these things or not. If you're interested in knowing more about them and their philosophy, read on.

CHAPTER II

What is Yoga?

FRIENDS and acquaintances have often said to me, " I'd like to learn *all* about Yoga," and when I've answered, " Yes, I'm sure," in a non-commital manner, they popped the inevitable question, " How can I start?"

Before starting the study of yoga one should have some idea of the vast scope of the subject. The student should be made to realise that it is impossible to study every branch of yoga in Britain, for a great deal about it cannot be assimilated either through books or lectures. It has to be learnt at the feet of a *guru* or teacher, and through bitter personal experience.

It is harder for almost any European to become a yogi than it is for a Civil Service department to make an instant decision, or for a Minister of State to give a direct answer at Question Time. As far as Europeans are concerned, the process is an unnatural one. The disciple or *chela* must renounce all earthly possessions and sunder all family ties. Heredity, birth, schooling, ancestry, environment, tradition are all against it. One must learn to think clearly, a process few are capable of. We must learn not to confuse the essential with the irrelevant.

But I assume that most readers do not desire to become yogis, but merely to acquire some of the physical, mental and spiritual qualities that yogis possess.

Most people cling to the utterly erroneous idea that yoga is some sort of system of physical exercises; a system that requires the pupil to contort his limbs into the weirdest and most intricate positions, which only ballet dancers, acrobats and the boneless can hope to achieve. This belief has gained currency because of some yoga exercises described on the television, and pictures of yoga students that sometimes appear in the National Press. These people are merely practising that branch of yoga which deals with the physical side, and it is with this branch, known as Hatha Yoga, that most people are concerned, and about which the greater part of this book is about.

Hatha Yoga helps one to be physically fit, and it can be practised to the exclusion of all other forms of yoga. To become a yogi it is essential first to practise Hatha Yoga, for unless the body is fit, it is impossible to forget it and concentrate upon the mind.

Yoga is more than a mere combination of exercises and breathing. These are merely a means towards an end. Nor does it involve, as some imagine, sitting for endless hours contemplating one's navel, or the Infinite.

Yoga is a complete philosophy of life. It embraces the physical, mental and spiritual. It is non-sectarian, and the religious as well as the non-religious can study yoga with benefit and without offence to their beliefs or disbeliefs. The Rationalist, the Atheist, the Agnostic—all can be yogis. So too can the Catholic, the Hindu, the Moslem, the Jew or the believer in any Mumbo-Jumbo. Yoga does not ask him to believe in anything to which his reason does not subscribe.

Thus, there is a vast gulf between " becoming a yogi," and practising some " form of yoga." You can practise yoga without giving up your job, leaving your wife or parting with your most cherished possessions. You can travel part of the way and see some of the scenery, but you cannot achieve the ultimate goal. Many explain that they have responsibilities to parents, wives, children and relatives; responsibilities they cannot lightly relinquish. Such persons cannot become yogis, but they can make their lives fuller and happier by studying and practising such branches of yoga philosophy suited to their temperament.

The true yogi says—and rightly so—that Man came into the world alone and without being consulted and as such owes neither moral nor material debt to anyone. He can therefore relinquish all responsibilities without a twinge of conscience.

Here I must explain that the words " conscience," " moral," " truth," " good," and " bad " are meaningless to the yogi. When we speak about " good " and " bad " things, we do not use the words in their absolute sense, but use them relatively. Betting and thieving, for instance, are neither good nor bad in themselves, but in relation to circumstances and the society and the times in which we find ourselves.

The compleat yogi disassociates himself from all these extraneous influences. They have been seeking absolute truth for countless centuries, and like our philosophers in the west are no nearer the solution.

No one knows exactly when yoga was first propounded. It is certainly neither the oldest nor the only philosophy to emerge from India. Many schools of philosophy have flourished, the most famous being Nyaya, Vaisesika, Samkhya, Yoga, Mimamsa and Vedanta. They are all developments of the *Upanishads* (secret teachings); that portion of the *Vedas* (one of the four earliest compositions of the Aryans) devoted to philosophy. The Upanishads were written in all probability somewhere about the eighth century B.C. and the Vedas developed some six hundred and fifty years later.

The six classical systems I have named possess a common denominator, but ultimately Samkhya and Yoga became recognised as the most important. Between the two there is a close similarity, the main difference being that Samkhya deals with the universal condition of Nature, whereas Yoga with the individual condition of Nature.

It is impossible in a mere chapter to do more than begin to explain the immense complications of the Yoga system of philosophy, and I shall limit myself to outlining some of the branches of Yoga, and describing how some of the ancient religious beliefs and philosophies were handed down.

Unfortunately there seems to be no pure stream of yoga teaching. It is so adulterated and diluted with religious beliefs and supersitition that most students from the west soon find themselves bogged down in a mass of unimportant detail that reason tells them must be useless, and many become discouraged and relinquish their studies. It requires considerable perspicacity to enable one to shift the chaff from the wheat.

Many scholars and archæologists believe that the earliest civilisation existed somewhere in Mesopotamia, a civilisation earlier even than that of China, and that these people spread gradually to Central Asia. It was their ancestors, known as Aryans, who invaded India about 3,000 B.C. and imposed their culture on the aborigines. In the course of time they evolved a literature inevitably of a religious character, the first compositions of which were the Vedas or sacred writings. *Veda* is derived from the Sanskrit " *vid*," *to know*.

Ancient India had no writing, so all teachings were memorised, and the highest castes—Brahmins—were selected to learn these teachings and hand them down. It was their sacred prerogative. But without phenomenal memories it would have proved a task beyond the ability of any human being. From their very earliest years they were put through a rigorous course of memory training. This was necessary, for the Rig-Veda, which is the oldest of the four Vedas and the most ancient piece of Indo-European literature in existence, consists of 1,017 poems, comprising 10,550 verses and contains altogether no fewer than 153,826 words—a feat likely to tax the finest memory.

There remained the other Vedas and the rest of the Upanishads as well; but there are many Brahmins in India who can repeat the lot from memory. A special body came into being known as *stotrayas,* or professional Vedic students, whose job it was to memorise these works, so that if suddenly all the ancient books of India were destroyed by fire or atomic explosion, one of these men, if saved, could reproduce the entire literature from memory!

Auadhani, a Hindu who lived in Bombay before the war, knew the Vedas by heart. He could memorise any poem in any language after hearing it once, and could repeat from memory 1,000 sentences after once hearing or reading them.

For the entrance examination of the El Hazar University, Cairo, students are required to repeat the entire Quran, which is about as long as the New Testament, from memory.

This gift of memory is not exclusively Indian, or for that matter Eastern, for some Europeans have given proof of remarkable memories, too. But when writing had not been invented, people were forced to memorise and developed marvellous memories. The Maoris, an ancient and cultured race, have a considerable literature of their own, and in the past much of it was committed to memory because they had no script, and because they feared that written records might be destroyed.

Their chiefs used to be trained along the lines of the Brahmin stotrayas. Years ago when a Land Commission visited New Zealand, their Chief Kaumataua held the members spellbound for three days while he recited the history and descent of his tribes through thirty-four generations, extending over a period of a thousand years, a feat accomplished without the aid of a single note.

In India the gift of memory is cultivated for its own sake, as a thing to be cherished. The study of yoga is an excellent aid to memory, for yoga develops the ability to concentrate, and concentration makes memorising easy.

Among other things the yogis claim that Jesus Christ was one of them. They cite his disappearance into the desert, his fasting and temptation as example of yoga precept. Yogis with whom I have spoken say: " What does any one in Europe or America know of Christ's life between the ages of twelve and thirty? Where was he? What was he doing? Why did he not marry in a land where men marry early and take many wives? How did he, a carpenter's son, suddenly become endowed with miraculous powers?" It certainly seems logical to contend that Jesus wandered through the Holy Land seeking teachers, hearkening to the wise men, and gaining knowledge and power. We know that he fasted, meditated and concentrated, just as yogis do, away from the haunts of men. He urges men not to lay up treasure " that moth and rust doth corrupt," and " to sell all and give to the poor." Just the things that yogis do.

Take away the myth of the virgin birth: strip his life story of all the mystery with which it is enshrouded, and Jesus stands revealed as another Eastern mystic, such as yogis are. But as in the case of the genuine yogi, one has to seek far and wide to find men who follow the teachings of their master.

All effective systems of philosophy, all sound systems of living, and all powerful religions are essentially simple. They begin to crumble when they become complicated. Christianity is a striking example. There is one law only: Love your neighbour as yourself.

What have we in our wisdom done with this simple admonition? Have we been content merely to love our neighbours? No.

We have erected a complicated clerical hierarchy. We have built, at enormous cost, vast cathedrals and churches into which people seldom go unless they are being married, baptised or having the burial service pronounced over them. And there is not one Christian Church, but many: Roman Catholics, Anglicans, Protestants, Wesleyans, Baptists, Methodists, Holy Rollers, Four Square Gospellers, Coglers, Plymouth Brethren, Presbyterians, and some three or four *hundred* other varieties. Some wear elaborate vestments, others swing incense and toll bells, some bow, some kneel, others roll on the floor. There is variety enough to suit every taste. You pay your money and take your choice.

All this complicated rigmarole came about because two thousand years ago the son of a carpenter told his disciples to love one another.

What is more, most of these sects either hate or despise some of the others, if not all. And this animosity extends to all fields of activity among the more rabid communities. One has only to buy a ticket for a Rangers v. Celtic football match to witness an extraordinary display of Christian unity and brotherly love.

Nor are the Christians the only religious sects that behave in this way. Hindu and Moslem do it, too; and Jew and Gentile.

In practice the genuine yogi carries out the only Christian precept that matters; love all men. Organised religion pays lip service to Christ's teachings, and even ministers of religion show little intention of executing his commands literally. They indulge in all sorts of sophistries to get round the unpleasant and difficult teachings of Christ. Christ, they say, never meant them to be taken literally. Christ spoke in parables. And so on. Even the Roman Catholic clergy, who prate the virtues of poverty, live on a more luxurious scale than most other priests, and certainly in greater affluence than many of the laity. They do not, perhaps, possess large sums of ready money. But they are often seen in expensive places, eating well, drinking good wine, smoking excellent cigars and enjoying the other amenities of life with a gusto that most laymen envy. Because perhaps of their clear consciences.

None of these acts is in itself reprehensible, but they go ill with the constant preaching of poverty.

Just as it is rare to find Christians who practise Christianity, so is it equally rare to find yogis who carry out all the precepts of their cult. Thus, it is rare to come across a yogi with truly miraculous powers.

Men who set out to be yogis are every bit as corruptible as men who set out to be Christians, or bankers, or politicians. In the course of the many centuries since yoga was first established, millions have embraced yoga and tried to modify or corrupt it to suit their ends, and that is why the principles and ways of one sect of yogis seems sometimes to clash with those of another sect of yogis—for, just as there are different kinds of Christians, so too are there different kinds of yogis.

No one is quite sure who founded Yoga philosophy. No one knows whether one man thought it all out, or whether it evolved gradually over a period of centuries. This second theory seems the more feasible, for Yoga is so vast a study that it seems improbable that any one man, or even a number of men, could, in the course of a single lifetime, have synthesised so much wisdom.

Scholars possess tidy minds and hate to leave the ends of any theory untied; so most of them have agreed that it was Patanjali who was responsible for collecting and correlating the teachings of the first yogis, and it was he who presented them in the form of his famous Sutras, or aphorisims: *Yogasutra*. So little is known about Patanjali that historians are not even sure whether he is the grammarian of the same name who wrote the famous commentary, *Mahabhasya,* on the grammar of Panini, or another person. We like to believe that both works were written by the same man. But, in any case, the point is one of mere academic interest.

As this is not a book dealing with the science of Yoga, but merely contains interesting facts about it, and guides those who wish to delve deeply, I shall not say something about the various branches of Yoga. It is a common fallacy to think that because one is a Yogi one instantly becomes a worker of miracles and a master of magic.

Masters of yoga are extremely rare, but yogis of every degree abound.

There are many branches: Hatha, Raja, Gnana, Karma, Bhakta, Laya, Lignan-Yoni, Kundalini, Tantra, and other forms.

When Europeans and Americans talk about Yoga, they usually mean Hatha Yoga, that type dealing with the body. Yogis insist that unless the body is fit, the mind cannot function to its full capacity. It loses in efficiency. They say that the mind, body and spirit are interdependent, and just as a sick body can affect the mind, so can a sick mind affect the body and the spirit, and an unhealthy spirit has an adverse effect upon mind and body. This interaction of body, mind and spirit was not generally accepted by either philosophers or scientists in Europe until a few years ago, and even to-day there is no unanimity on the subject.

In primitive communities physical fitness is a prime asset, for only by physical fitness and prowess does one eat and exist. Consequently the Ancient Aryans set immense store on fitness and strength. The Hymn of Rudra goes: "We bow before ye who are strength incarnate. We bow before ye who are the giver of strength, and we bow before ye who are also the suppressor of strength," for there were two uses to which strength could be put—good and evil.

In the Mandukya Upanishad one reads: "Intellectual development and learning are of no avail . . . so long as the physique is weak." But strength must always be a medium through which good service must be carried out, and not used either to exploit or suppress. In the ancient literature of India there are many references to strength; but it is also stressed that strength must never be misused.

The yoga idea of strength differs from that of the European. We regard massive muscles as a sign of strength, and photographs of European and American strong men usually show them in unnatural positions, flexing their biceps or other prominent groups of muscles.

The yogis say, however, that no one is strong unless his heart, lungs, brain, liver, kidneys, his sense, his faculties of speech and hearing, his sense of touch and all other parts of the body function properly. A man is not strong if his internal organs are weak, for the yogis say that internal strength is preferable to big muscles and bulk. Bulk is, in fact, often a handicap.

They say that the period of youth extends from sixteen to seventy years of age and only after that should middle age set in gradually. A man should live for at least one hundred years without loss of either muscular or functional ability, and the normal span of life should be one hundred and fifty years.

We imagine that a massive physique is necessarily a powerful one, but the yogis say that often a thin body is strong, whereas a big, muscular one may be weak. They lay stress on the importance of vitality and stamina, not on mere ox-like strength.

All these ideas are expounded clearly in the Ayurveda, which, centuries before scientists even considered such factors, stated that health and fitness were determined by heredity, the food and climate of one's native country, environment, and mode of living. The physical exercises a man follows should be designed with such factors in view.

The more one reads about and delves into yoga, the more one is astounded by the very modern ideas held by these philosophers of many centuries ago, and scholars sometimes wonder why they did not, with the learning they possessed, produce a race of supermen. They failed because the complete philosophy is so difficult and so arduous that few can stay the course. Many corrupted the teachings for personal gain.

Yoga neither adopts nor embraces external aids. Yogis say that everything a man needs for perfection lies within himself if only he knows how to use it rightly.

Physical culture experts of the European school believe in intense activity to increase the circulation of the blood. This accelerates breathing, but also results in rapid muscular fatigue. Impurities are thrown off by the lungs and through the skin, and fresh stores of oxygen purify the blood and help to invigorate the system.

Yoga obtains the same results without violent physical activity. Both circulation as well as pulse beat can be accelerated by means of stationary poses known as yogasanas; because of this yoga is ideal for the aged, the infirm, those suffering from high blood pressure and valvular diseases of the heart.

One of the first signs of increasing age is stiffness. Another is lumbago. You bend and get fixed in a position from which it is painful to straighten up. Yogasanas aim at keeping the body elastic, and the spine curved naturally, as it should be. Many European systems aim at straightening the spine—why, it is difficult to say, for Nature did not design the spine in the shape of a ramrod.

It is strange that in Europe a man who walks like a poker is admired because of his " erect carriage."

Everything about the yoga system of exercises is up-to-date. Those who thought out the system of yogasanas ensured by their practise an adequate supply of blood to the endocrine glands centuries before any western scientist even knew that such glands existed, or suspected that they affect vitality, intelligence, or the growth of certain limbs or organs. They even studied the nervous system and evolved postures and breathing exercises to keep it working efficiently.

They were vigorous opponents of the popular mass-muscle school which had thousands of adherents to their every one. You can see and feel and admire excessively big muscles. They give the frame a pleasing appearance and the owner the illusion of vast controlled power.

The yogis know that whereas the shell of a nut may be unblemished, the core may be rotten.

They investigated colour, vibrations, thought-transference and many of the phenomena that scientists are now studying for the first time. They were masters of metaphysics and seekers after absolute truth. Constantly they asked questions for which in other countries men would have been roasted alive. They followed such ideas as appealed to their reason, rejecting all others. Or rather, a few did so. Thousands took the easy path.

They had no script, and this is one reason why many of their teachings have been handed down in adulterated form. It may seem sheer heresy for me to say so, but a good deal of so-called yoga ritual seems to me to have degenerated into sheer mumbo-jumbo, just as it is with other cults and religions. Christianity, for instance, as Christ laid it down, fails to mention the ringing of bells, the lighting of candles, constant genuflexions, the swinging of incense, the repetition of meaningless litanies and sevenfold *amens* which have no more connection with Christianity than " boxing the compass " with the prize ring.

A great deal that passes for yoga cannot be explained, but its devotees are so fanatical that they will do almost anything that has been done for ages, or is printed in black and white in a book. As few people used their brains for thinking in the old days as they do now.

I have had long discussions with yogis on such matters, but have been given no satisfying explanation. In the course of centuries there has doubtless been much corruption of the original ideas. There are many sects of yogis, all of whom agree on the fundamentals of their philosophy, but differ in detail. And—this will surprise most people in Britain—there are yogis who marry! Others own property; and there are even female yogis.

Such yogis: the female, the married and the property owners are regarded by those who take the vow of celibacy and renounce worldly possessions as not genuine yogis— not the real MacKay—though it must be admitted that even these sometimes exhibit extraordinary powers.

If, as most readers who are intrigued will do, you content yourself with a study of elementary Hatha Yoga, none of these details will either disturb or affect you. It is only when you delve deeply into the subject and come across a great many conflicting ideas and statements; when you must decide how much is truth and how much supersititon; how much scientific and how much religious, that you are apt to be confused. Those who want some practical benefit from yoga—and most of you who read this will—

must ignore a vast amount of yogic lore. Like all ancient lore, it is inextricably mixed with religion and superstition which passes for mysticism and erudition.

A few men have devoted their lives to selecting the pearls in this vast and indiscriminate higgledy-piggledy mass of information. With yoga, as with other subjects, use your reason, judgment and commonsense. Do not hesitate to discard that which does not appeal to your reason, for yoga is not a species of magic, however much some of its devotees might desire it so to be. Because of this attitude, charlatans abound, and it has fallen into disrepute.

Yoga does not require blind belief. It is a reasoned philosophy, and its followers reject anything that cannot be proved. For everything that one is required to do there is a sound reason, though sometimes that reason is not quite plain. In which case one has to abide by results. But if the reason is not forthcoming and the result is not satisfactory, something must be wrong with the method.

Many of the instructions, if carefully and patiently followed, bring positive benefits in their train. That alone justifies them being done. Others seem merely to be part of some meaningless ritual devised to impress students of a more impressionable age. Omit them.

Remember that few—exceedingly few indeed—who write about Yoga, practise it. Gentlemen calling themselves Yoga This and Swami That, who have never been to India except in the Army or some trade concern, or even in imagination, pretend to be experts in yoga. Many have never spoken to a yogi, except one of those smooth, sleek, saffron-gowned, glib-tongued lecturers who make a good living in America. They have all the vague jargon on the tips of their tongues and impress thousands of incredulous females.

47

Of one thing you can be sure, the man who makes a fat income purveying yoga is not a genuine yogi, for one of the five objects which stand in the way of attainment is *desire*.

Some explanation is necessary about the different branches into which yoga is divided, though it must be stressed that all these are inter-related. They are not complete branches that can be studied independently; each must be studied and practised in conjunction with others. Hatha yoga, for instance, which deals in its early stages entirely with the body, is the basis of all yoga, for without a fit body it is impossible to make any appreciable progress. By fit, I mean fit in the yoga sense—so free from aches and pains and illnesses that one is able to forget the body and concentrate on the mind and on spiritual matters.

Because of its comparative simplicity, Hatha yoga attracts most Europeans.

According to yogi lore and teachings body, mind and spirit are all of the same stuff; and are merely different forms of the same stuff. This idea in no way differs from modern scientific thought and is endorsed by men like Jeans, Eddington, Millikan and others. Bertrand Russell says: " So long as we adhere to the conventional notions of mind and matter, we are condemned to a view of perception that is miraculous. . . .

" Everything that we can directly observe of the physical world happens inside our heads, and consists of mental events in at least one sense of the word *mental*. It also consists of events which form part of the physical world. The development of this point of view will lead us to the conclusion that the distinction between mind and matter is illusory. The stuff of the world may be called physical or mental or both or neither as we please; in fact, the words serve no purpose."

The old idea, accepted by the West for centuries, that mind and body and spirit are three separate entities which have no connection, was rejected by the authors of the yoga system of philosophy long before the dawn of our civilisation. They also reject the idea that the mind can work efficiently if the body is either dangerously sick or seriously injured. " There was never yet philosopher could endure the toothache patiently!" (Much Ado V. 1). Violent aches and pains must interfere with concentration and human efficiency.

An immense volume of valuable work has been done by men either permanently in pain or suffering from some chronic and painful disease. For nearly forty years Charles Darwin never knew one day of real health; on bad days he suffered from " swimming in the head." He stammered and could not pronounce certain words. Flaubert was an epileptic. Joule, who discovered the mechanical equivalent of heat, was not only deformed but suffered from a severe disease of the brain, which eventually killed him. Galileo suffered from chronic disorders, pains in the body, insomnia and loss of appetite. Luther lived in a world of terrible toothache and neuralgia. Curzon was strapped in a strait jacket and was always in pain. The list is almost endless. Great men have accomplished great things, *despite*, not because of, pain and illness.

We like to think of the mind as a superior entity which uses the body as its instrument. Some people even divide pleasure into two classes: refined and crude. They class music, poetry and such diversions as mental pleasures, and as such, refined. They bracket eating, drinking and the making of physical love as coarse *physical* pleasures; forgetting that both mind and body enter into both types. Without a physical ear and an eardrum; without the nervous system which passes messages to the brain; without a brain itself, music and poetry would mean nothing to us. Both also give us considerable physical exhilaration. The whole idea that mind and body are distinct and separate is ridiculous and has no scientific basis whatsoever. There is always an interaction of mind and body, and neither pleasure nor pain is either wholly physical or mental, but a blend of both.

If the mind is a superior entity having no connection with the body, what happens to it when you receive a severe blow on the head and are knocked unconscious? Does it continue to function independently of the body? When the body dies there is no evidence that the mind functions as it did during life, spiritualists notwithstanding.

Ah, say some; but the spirit keeps going. By spirit I suppose one means that vital force that makes the works go round when one is alive. True; if it is matter, as the yogis say, it cannot be destroyed. But the body changes shape after death, disintegrates into other forms of matter and ultimately into gases. So, for all we know, do the mind and spirit. About this I should not dream of being dogmatic, for not even the wisest scientist knows what happens when we die.

The yogis have not wholly explained the mystery of life, at any rate to my satisfaction. Or if they have, my mind is unable to grasp the truths they expound, for much that they say is wrapped up in so many symbolic phrases and imagery that I have been unable to sift the gold from the dross. For this I blame my limited intelligence, and not the yogis. But from what I have seen and read I know they possess a far greater degree of control over both mind and body than we, and as their age-old theories of interaction of body, mind and spirit are in keeping with modern ideas, I have a considerable amount of respect for them and feel that they should be investigated by western scientists.

When a man like Prime Minister Nehru does yoga exercises each morning, Jung and Einstein praise the philosophy, and Aldous Huxley admits its value, then it is high time for UNESCO also to investigate it.

I trust I have shown that concentration on purely physical activities will not enable you to make as much progress as you wish in yoga. Once you have mastered the *elementary* stages of Hatha Yoga, in order to gain results the mind must be called into play, and both meditation as well as concentration must be practised.

There are four main forms of yoga: Hatha yoga, Raja yoga, Laya yoga, and Mantra yoga; but also various subsidiary forms such as Bhakti, Karma, Jnana, Yantra, Khyana, Shakti, Samadhi, Yoni and Kundalini.

Hatha yoga, as I have stated earlier, is the kind that interests most people in this country, and, in fact, is the kind of yoga best suited to most Europeans. It is positive. The word Hatha is a combination of the syllables " ha," meaning " Sun," and " tha," meaning " moon." The word is symbolic, representing the union of two great worlds; in the case of Man, his ego with the universe.

The object of Hatha is to cleanse and purify the physical body, both inside and out; to give the body strength and stamina, and to train it to endure changes of climate and environment.

Hatha yoga teaches something that has long been forgotten in Europe and America; the value of remaining still and calm and patient, which helps to build up personal confidence. There are many physical and mental benefits to be gained by the regular and meticulous practice of Hatha yoga, and in the very advanced stages such apparent miracles as levitation can be achieved. To accomplish this, however, the student must travel to India and place himself in the hands of a competent Guru or teacher. It will be impossible for him to continue his normal life.

Hatha yoga includes such practices as daily hygiene, internal as well as external; a sort of hygiene which people in Britain know nothing about. It includes also yogasanas, or postures, which ensure a proper supply of blood to all parts of the body, strengthen the spine and internal organs and assist the circulation. Then there are the " mudras," a very advanced system of physical exercises that give one control of the abdominal and other important groups of muscles essential to perfect health. Pranayama (prana, breath; yama, cessation) or breath control increases fitness and immunity from changes of temperature and disease; pratyahara (prati, towards; har, to hold back) is that branch of Hatha yoga that helps to develop patience; dharana (dhar, to hold) develops powers of concentration; dhyana (dhyai, to think) are practices which assist one to meditate.

Then there is Raja yoga, by which the student is able to gain a true understanding of himself. It is a form of study which in simple terms may be described as Yoga psychology, and its aim is to raise the character to its highest peak of development.

Laya yoga, or Layakrika yoga, helps one to gain such a mastery of the nerve centres as to make him a master, and not a tool of his senses.

Mantra yoga is the yoga of sound and vibration. It will appeal strongly to musicians and those who love form, colour and ritual. Much of it conforms amazingly with modern ideas on vibration.

It is impossible to get the utmost out of Hatha yoga without some understanding of Raja yoga and Laya yoga, for the mind and nerve centres are part of the body, and if they do not function efficiently, the body necessarily suffers. Raja yoga itself is a synthesis of Bhakti, which is a form of worship, Karma and Jnana yogas. An explanation of these types would not only be pointless at this stage, but positively confusing, for it is impossible to give cut and dried explanations in a few lines. As it is, the little that I have said, and said as simply as possible, must be confusing to those who have so far no knowledge of yoga.

Kundalini yoga, for instance, is an advanced form of Hatha yoga and is almost impossible to master from books or written lessons. But when mastered, the benefits are well nigh incredible. Without expert guidance, however, Kundalini practices might be dangerous.

It is sufficient to say that a European, devoting an hour each day to Hatha yoga, with such of the other forms as impinge on it, will have enough to study and sufficient to practise to keep him occupied for the remainder of a fairly long life. Few people can spare more than fifteen or twenty minutes a day on Hatha yoga, but even in this short period one can become fitter, immune from disease, and gain a serene and unworried outlook.

There is a form of yoga known as Tantric or Tantrik. It is an advanced form, the teachings of which are written in the 64 volumes of the Tantra, and it is difficult to study unless one journeys to Tibet. And how many of us can venture into that Forbidden Land?

The yoga of the Goraknathis, or followers of Goraknath, and the Kanphatas (yogis who split the cartilage of the ear for the purpose of wearing earrings) is Hatha. Tantric is favoured by the Buddhist element, which is much stronger in Tibet than in India. In Tibet it is practised in the pure form, but in India, and especially Bengal, where it has a considerable vogue, it has become corrupted and confused with religion, and has for some years been associated with gruesome and repulsive religious rites.

There is a considerable Tantric literature available in this country, but I should not advise any student of yoga to follow the study unless he has first mastered a good deal more than the mere fundamentals of Hatha Yoga; otherwise he will inevitably become discouraged and confused.

The ideal conditions for the practice of yoga, as laid down by the ancient texts, are almost impossible for the ordinary British student, for Hatha yoga should be practised in a private cell (difficult with the present housing shortage) free from stones, fire and water, standing in a well-governed country (is ours well governed?) free from violence, where the citizens are law abiding and alms abundant. This perhaps comes within the scope of our all-embracing social services. There are all sorts of other conditions; the cell must have a small door, must be free from vermin and stand in a lovely garden. With our limited facilities, however, it is enough to urge that your yoga exercises and breathing shall be carried out, if possible, alone and in a well aired room. A great deal can be achieved even if conditions are not ideal.

CHAPTER III

Yoga Hygiene

YOGA lays considerable stress on physical fitness, and perfect fitness cannot be achieved unless your body is clean. Because in very ancient India there was no written code, instruction had to be memorised and observed in the form of ritual. Thus, personal hygiene was made a rite, as it is in more than one religion. The Jews and the Moslems, for instance, observe certain strict rules about the washing of hands and feet, and the Bible lays down that cleanliness is next to godliness, though in the Middle Ages hermits, saints and recluses turned a blind eye to this injunction and the cult of dirt had a distinct vogue.

When the Roman Empire—where bathing reached a fine art—fell, bathing became synonymous with Evil in the minds of devout Christians, and all over Europe there was a powerful reaction against immersing the body in water. Pious Christians came to feel that washing was wicked, and thereafter they deliberately cultivated not only dirt, but vermin. The cassock of St. Francis, we are told, was sticky with filth and alive with vermin; and there are vivid accounts of the state of Thomas à Becket's undervest. History relates that Cardinal Bellarmine welcomed vermin on the grounds that as they have no future life we should give them a pleasant time in this world!

Christians fondly imagined that a state of filth pleased the Almighty far better than if they washed, and Lecky says that a clean body was regarded as one of the worst forms of vanity and pollution of the soul.

There is no doubt about the piety of St. Anthony, for he never washed his feet; another exceedingly devout hermit named Abraham so neglected cleaning his face that it was said that the purity of his soul shone out from it. And St. Augustine, who for those times must have seemed a finicky old maid, advised gentlemen to wash " about once a month." He had little in common with St. Jerome, whose face was so caked with dirt that he resembled a negro.

Centuries later, even so civilised a man as Dr. Johnson confessed: " I do not love immersion," and Pepys wrote that when he and his wife were given a bed riddled with fleas they were " very merry." When Lady Mary Montague was told her hands were filthy, she exclaimed: " My hands! You should see my feet! "

Perhaps a period will come again when there will be a revulsion against the present ungodly trend in cleanliness, and Europe will revert to dirt. Who knows?

The Hindus have always been a clean race, an easy enough matter in a warm climate, but even among them we find mystics who cover their bodies with filth because they labour under the impression that it is a holy and meritorious thing to do.

Yoga teachings lay down firmly and with no equivocation that in order to be fit one must also be clean, both inside as well as out. Their code of hygiene, developed centuries ago, is based on strictly scientific lines.

To the yogi fitness does not mean the avoidance of illness. It denotes a state where one is buoyant and tingling with vitality. It is a man's duty to remain fit. Disease is a sin, and a violation of the principles of living. The person who maltreats his body is a criminal and should be locked up and given a course of treatment during detention.

Yoga hygiene has five main aims: fitness, purity of the body, eradication of disease, longevity, and spiritual and moral elevation.

Yoga hygiene starts as soon as you awake.

Most people who suffer from headaches and mild stomach and other disorders do not realise that one of the worst habits is the modern one of drinking tea in bed; not because drinking tea is a wicked act, either in bed or out, but because the mouth and the teeth are unclean when you awake.

Use a tooth brush regularly and change it as soon as the bristles begin to sag. Earlier, if you like. The brushes used by even clean and educated people make one shudder.

After using the brush rinse it thoroughly in scalding water, otherwise it becomes an excellent germ carrier.

Yoga *dantadhouti,* or purification of the mouth, has been endorsed by numerous medical authorities—especially that section devoted to the cleaning of the tongue.

Advertisements in books and magazines tell us that had breath is the result of not using this or that tooth paste or mouth wash. This is untrue. Breath becomes foul either because your tongue is filthy and coated and your inside like a sewer; or both.

In the morning your tongue is coated with a white, or if your stomach is dirty, with a yellow layer. Unless you scrub your tongue before taking your early morning cup of tea, you wash this decomposing epithelium into your stomach, and in a month the cumulative effect of this poison is sufficient to give you headaches or that listless feeling which so many are compelled to fight.

Rub your tongue with your tooth brush. This may seem a trifle harsh at first, but you will soon grow accustomed to it. Yogis also cleanse the root of the tongue by pushing the tongue out, placing two or three fingers at the root of the tongue and scraping it. This practice is known as *jivhamulasodhanam*. Try it, and you will be astonished at the quantity of mucous deposited on your tongue each night.

Wash teeth and tongue at least twice daily; on rising, and before going to bed.

There is no reason for not returning to bed to read the morning papers and have your tea *after* washing your mouth and tongue, but somehow I feel you may not want to.

Washing eyes, nose and ears are also strict yoga observances. Most people swish round their faces and feel that eyes, ears and nose have been taken in during this all round performance. But they haven't.

The number of persons who suffer from deafness is astounding, and seventy per cent. of deafness, so doctors tell us, is psychological. Some of it is caused because the defensive mechanism of the body shuts out sound; this is fairly common in industrial areas where people work in an atmosphere of noise. In such areas there is a tremendous amount of dust and dirt in the air, and a good deal of this finds its way into the ears, sealing them effectively.

Each time you wash your face, gently massage the back of the base of the ear. This loosens any wax that may form. Then gently screw the ends of the little fingers into the ears and vibrate them by moving the fingers up and down rapidly. Do likewise when you dry your ears— with a fine towel. A clean ear does not accumulate wax, and if washed regularly, you will have no difficulty in hearing clearly.

Buy a small syringe and once a month syringe your ears carefully, but not too gently, with water at a temperature between 105-115 degrees Fah. The yogis call this ear hygiene *karnarandhra dhouti*. There is also another and more elaborate process known as *neti* by which the middle ear can be reached, but this is so advanced and complicated that there is little point in outlining it here.

Not many people make a point of washing their nostrils each time they wash, or for that matter, once a day. One of the most effective ways of cleaning the air passages is by doing the yoga exercise *kapalabhati,* which will be described in the chapter on breathing. But, the nostrils can also be cleansed by sniffing water. When as children we inadvertently sniff water into the nostrils, there is usually a sudden, burning sensation, which causes us to desist and take good care never to repeat the indiscretion.

Yoga outlines three methods of nasal cleansing: *vyuthrama,* or the act of sniffing up water through both nostrils and expelling it through the mouth, for the nasal passages are connected to the mouth; *sitkrama,* sucking water in through the mouth and out through the nostrils; and *siddha*—a far more difficult feat—sniffing water in through one nostril and out through the other nostril by way of the mouth.

The novice who does this will inevitably feel a painful burning sensation at the back of the nostrils. You've got to train your nose, just as you have to train any other part of your body, so the best way to start is by using salt water.

Fill a cup with warm water. Mix a little salt into it—just how much, you will decide by experiment. Too much burns the nostrils and is harsh; too little is ineffective. Close one nostril and sniff the salt solution up through the other. Then close the other nostril and blow the water out through the first. Sniff and blow alternately through each nostril and you will find that even if your nose was blocked before, you will now be able to breathe with comparative freedom. This is known as *jalaneti;* it removes accumulated and hardened mucous, clears the air passages, and if practised from childhood would prevent adenoids.

If other measures for health are observed and *jalaneti* is done regularly, it will be difficult to catch cold. Later, when you get used to sniffing warm salt solution, try sniffing plain cold water, for this hardens the air passages. Cold water, whether taken inside or out, helps to toughen your body and increase its resistance to disease.

Though few people realise it, blocked nostrils are the prelude to all sorts of diseases, among which are headaches, eyestrain and enlarged tonsils. Keep your nostrils clean and massage the root of the nose—near the eyes—to ensure the free flow of blood. This is even more important in the case of one who wears spectacles.

Care of the eyes comes within the scope of Yoga hygiene, and is known as *trakta.* The eyes are a barometer of health; puffy eyelids or bags under the eyes are a sure sign either of heart trouble or kidney trouble; dark rings round the eyes indicate either a bad circulation or nervous exhaustion—one reason why dark rings appear after a number of late nights in succession—and, in fact, all sorts of minor and major troubles make themselves apparent first by some sign in the eyes. Before the war there arose a school of physicians in Germany who diagnosed disease entirely by looking into the eyes.

Most people seem to regard the eye as not a part of the body, but something apart. The eye is affected by the quality and circulation of the blood, just as any other organ; in fact, it is more sensitive to bodily changes than any other.

Examine the eye of an athlete in training and notice how bright and clear it is. The first modern to attach any importance to the condition of the eye was the famous physical culturist, Bernarr MacFadden.

Within recent years the eye bath has become popular and numerous proprietary eye lotions have found their way on to the market. If people only realised that eye health consists mainly in washing, massage, exercise and rest, they could dispense with all such lotions and save money.

After washing your face, fill your palms with cold water and slap the water gently on to the closed eyes. In winter, no matter how warm the water you wash in, always finish with cold. Women who value a smooth skin and glowing complexion will find that this simple treatment will do more than all the creams and lotions on the market.

Splashing with cold water invigorates the eyes and the skin. Try it this winter and see how it works. The shock at first may be considerable, but you will soon get used to it, and eventually so come to like the refreshing effect that you will never go without a cold splash.

Massage your eyes gently when you wash, and when during the day you feel eye-strain, close your eyes and cup them in your palms. This ancient yoga habit has recently been revived and publicised as if it were something new and revolutionary.

Yogis also practise sun and moon-gazing, which they claim strengthens the eyes. Gazing into the sun is a definite eye strengthener; but you must look at the sun only when it is climbing over the horizon or late in the evening as it is about to sink out of sight. Gaze at it until tears well into your eyes. Then stop.

Only benefit can accure if you practise this when the sun is rising or setting. Never, under any circumstances, try to look at the sun when it has gained strength. To do this at mid-day is folly, and results in blindness. Some years ago the Rajah of Aundh, who at 77 had the physique of a young man, claimed that he was able to dispense with the wearing of spectacles after practising eye-splashing, massage, sun gazing, and eye exercises.

Moon gazing strengthens the eyes, too, but there are few occasions in England when one can do this.

Yogis have numerous eye exercises and means of strengthening the eyes, but as they do not come within the orbits of hygiene, I shall deal with some of them when talking about meditation and concentration.

All that I have written on hygiene seems much too long to be put into practice every morning. Actually this is not so. Once you learn how to clean eyes, nose, ears and tongue, the complete routine can be accomplished in a matter of minutes. It's just practice and habit.

For centuries yogis have believed in the value of friction to make the skin fit. They use black-mud packs for their bodies, and wash their hair in black mud. Black mud is rubbed into the hair and scalp to remove dundruff and scurf—if any exists—and then rinsed off with water. Within recent years this same black mud has been exported in large quantities from India to the beauty saloons of America and Europe for use in mud-packs to beautify women. Those who pay through the nose for such beauty treatment may not realise it, but they are practising yoga methods of skin hygiene!

I do not advise the use of English mud for either friction or hair cleansing. Pure castile soap, or soft green soap is best. Wash your head at least once a week—more if you like. Sometimes I wash my head every day of the week, so dirty does it get in London. Dry the hair well, then brush vigorously with a stiff-bristled brush. Don't be afraid of the hair falling out. As you grow older some will, but new healthy hair will sprout in its place. Nor is it necessary to apply oil or grease to the hair. I don't. But for those who like oil, or must have it to keep their hair in place, I see no objection to a little being used.

And now a few words about bathing and the skin. A superstition exists in Britain, especially in mining areas, that washing the back weakens it, and I know of miners who refuse to immerse themselves in warm water for this very reason. But there is no evidence, medical or otherwise, to substantiate this theory. Immersion in very hot water does not weaken, provided you are used to it. The Japanese almost boil themselves daily and emerge from their communal baths looking like lobsters—and they are an extremely fit nation. But they always finish by rubbing with damp towels.

The yogis say that bathing is one means of cleansing the skin, and their teachings lay down rules for bathing in streams and rivers, and where these are not accessible in water from pure wells. In Britain tap water, which is pumped from pure sources, must of necessity serve our purpose. The yogis say little about warm baths because in India it is possible almost everywhere and at all times of the year to enjoy a cold bath. Even in areas where the temperature drops to freezing point the sun soon warms one, and cold water bathing if not enjoyable is at least bearable.

Bathing has two main functions. One is to clean; the other to innure the body to cold. The Channel swimmer, for instance, swims throughout the winter to harden his body and *put on weight*. If you are in good health and your digestion sound, immersion in cold water, progressively increased, will force your body to put on protective fat. Thus, the more you expose yourself —within reason—the more able you will be to withstand the rigours of winter.

Certain tribes of North American Indians walk bare-bodied long after the autumn chill has descended on the land. This so intrigued a traveller that he asked an Indian chief how he could bear to live with his body uncovered. The chief was surprised and pointed out that the traveller wore no clothes on his face.

'' But,'' expostulated the European, '' that's my face.''

'' Then,'' argued the chief logically, '' me all face.''

As stated earlier, in winter I have a very warm bath, because I like it. And for no other reason. We all have our little weaknesses; and I lie in the bath, reading, while my wife bangs on the door to tell me that the telephone is ringing, or that lunch is ready. When I've finished soaking I let the water out, soap myself and lie in cold water. While lying in cold water I find that the breathing exercise *bhastrika*, seems to generate heat, and can be done admirably while in a recumbent position. I can lie for five or ten minutes in cold water with no feeling of discomfort whatsoever, and when I emerge my body is covered with a glow of warmth.

For those who would experience the same *pleasure*, I say, " Go about it gradually—in easy stages."

You can be clean without bathing, provided you perspire sufficiently, though bathing is such a pleasant business that I cannot imagine anyone with a bath in the house doing without it. Your skin is a vital organ. You breathe through it, and get rid of poisons through the hundreds of thousands of tiny pores. Normally, a sedentary worker gets rid of about $2\frac{1}{2}$ pints of moisture through his pores. If you exercise violently and perspire profusely, even more poison exudes. The Ancient Greeks made quite a fetish of perspiring regularly; and all men who desired to keep healthy had to perspire freely at least once a day.

As this meant work and exercise, the Greeks were lean and thin waisted, and one of the most common terms of opprobrium was " fat." Nor does one see fat yogis. Or if they are fat, they are not genuine yogis.

If you want to remain healthy, it is essential that your skin breathes freely. There are several cases in history of men and boys dying because at the whim of some prince their skins were varnished with silver or gold leaf, thus sealing the pores.

C

You have two skins: the *epidermis* or upper layer, and the *dermis,* or true skin, beneath. The *dermis* is a loose tissue containing fat, blood vessels and nerves, and serves not only to protect the deeper structures underneath it, but to give shape and roundness to the body. It varies from about one fiftieth to one eighth of an inch in thickness, and is thicker in men than in women. It contains sweat glands varying in number from about 400 to 2,500 per square inch. The *epidermis* varies from one two hundredth to one twentieth of an inch in thickness; and is thicker and tougher on some parts of the body—palms and soles—than others.

When you wash frequently with very hot water and soap, the mouths of these sweat glands open and become choked with soap. Dust and dirt in the air make this soap black, and blackheads are the result. This is one reason why a cold bath should be taken immediately after a hot one; the pore ends close, squeezing out the soap. If you can't endure cold water, use lukewarm.

Few people have any idea how important a part the skin plays in keeping you fit. If you perspire sufficiently and wipe the perspiration away before it dries, bathing is not necessary, for the perspiration of a truly healthy person is not offensive. But if you do not at once either bathe or wipe off the perspiration, you are inviting trouble, for the exuding poisons seep back into the system and make you ill. Moreover, if perspiration is allowed to dry on you, the skin cools too rapidly, and you are likely to get a chill.

The condition of your skin is a sure indication of the state of your health. It should be fairly loose, and you should be able to grasp and lift it like the skin of a dog.

and it should glow with a satiny sheen. Many people with rosy cheeks have pasty unhealthy skins covering their bodies. During the war I saw thousands of men with such skins, through which impurities such as boils and pimples forced themselves. Their skins spoke eloquently of the bad diet of the army; where men were filled with potatoes, pastry and starches, and were starved of fruit, fresh green vegetables and necessary vitamins. Blame must not wholly be attached to the authorities, for fresh food was difficult to obtain; but even in peacetime the diet of the troops is just as stodgy.

Fresh air, hard work and exercise, and exposure of the skin to air and light did much to counteract the effect of this bad diet, and poisons were eliminated through the skin in the form of pimples, boils and carbuncles.

Your skin is a wonderful organ. It protects the organs inside you from exposure and infection; it regulates the temperature of the body; we breathe through our skins just as we breathe through nose and lungs. The skin is also extremely sensitive, and when the body is very sick, sensation sometimes ceases. Lepers, for instance, lose all sense of feeling. And when sensation increases intensely, it is a sure pointer to glandular or nervous disturbances.

For centuries the yogis have taken sun, air and water baths. They cost nothing. They have massaged the limbs and rubbed the skin with either bare hands or black mud. We term them "friction baths" and "mud" baths. You can give yourself a brisk friction bath any time you like with a hard nail brush; or if you wish to do it on a more expensive scale, buy a hair towel from the chemist (it will cost anything *from* half a guinea) and rub your body. Rub the skin briskly, though never hurt it; of course, you must use your commonsense and not rub the *epidermis* away.

The age-old system of the yogis, which has not changed one iota for nearly three thousand years, is a well nigh perfect one. Within the last fifty years doctors and scientists have *discovered* much that was known to these amazing people, as I shall point out in later chapters. Everything they did was done for an excellent reason, though sometimes those reasons have been forgotten. They even wore down their finger nails by rubbing them on rough stones, and they insisted on clean fingers, for it was with the fingers that they ate and touched their bodies.

CHAPTER IV

Yoga and Food

YOGIS pay great attention to the food they eat, for they contend that a man is what he eats. Nevertheless, they have such control over their bodies and stomachs that they can eat and digest any kind of food. Normally the yogi lives on less than a quarter of the amount eaten by the average European.

On moral as well as æsthetic grounds, yogis do not eat flesh. They consider it wrong to take life, and to eat flesh barbarous. The earth is plentifully supplied with green things: fruit, vegetables, cereals and nuts, so why should we recourse to slaughter to keep ourselves alive.

Like monks in monasteries, yogis rarely talk while eating. They eat slowly, either alone or in congenial company.

On the rare occasions when I dine or lunch out I am aghast at the speed at which people gobble their food. Often they shovel down their food as they talk rapidly. Sometimes a luncher sits at the next table, and while I am wading through one course, he eats an entire lunch and is gone. No wonder the sale of medicines and pills for allaying indigestion is on the increase, and one's neighbour's stomach ulcer an all-too-common and boring topic of conversation.

Fortunately, I am my own master and can choose my own rate of eating. Unhappily, most business people are not. They eat, meet friends and do their shopping during the lunch hour. And rather than go without lunch, or merely eat a snack, they gobble.

If you wish to gain some benefit from yoga, forget how to eat rapidly. Forego most of your lunch, if need be, but eat slowly and thoroughly. A little food masticated thoroughly nourishes you. A great deal, bolted, merely gives you a lump on your chest, a burning sensation inside, and a filthy temper. It ruins your digestion and makes you lethargic. No wonder most people feel absolutely done when they come back after lunch.

When you have mastered yoga, you can ignore the rules of sensible eating, and shovel down immense quantities of food at high speed. But then you won't want to.

You do not need a huge quantity of food to keep you in good health, or to maintain your strength. Let me give you a sample of my diet all last summer. Breakfast: weak tea—2, 3 or even 4 cups—without sugar. Or orange juice. Nothing else. Lunch: a plate of strawberries and ice cream; half a pound of cherries; a piece of cheese about 4 in. by 1 in. by ½ in.; two cups of good coffee; one or two pieces of dried fruit *or* preserved fruit *or* a few nuts *or* half a 2-oz. bar of milk chocolate. Tea: two or three cups of weak tea, 3 or 4 slices of very thin wholemeal bread and butter, and a slice of wholemeal fruit cake. Supper: salad, a potato baked in its skin, a cup of warm milk sweetened with molasses or black treacle. When strawberries and cherries are out of season, other fresh fruits take their place. When cream is available, we eat it in place of ice cream.

On our table lie such morning papers and magazines as have not as yet been read, or books that we may be reading at the time. My wife and I read throughout every meal—except when visitors are present. We talk when we feel like it, or read little bits aloud to each other if we feel they might be of interest. Lunch occupies anything from one and a half to two hours.

On this meagre diet both of us have gained a little weight this summer. My increase has been about eight pounds; this despite an active life, much walking and cycling, and cricket over the week ends. So when experts tell me that this or that number of calories is necessary for health, I know that they're talking rubbish. They've got their facts out of books written by other people who've got theirs out of other books; or by professors who've experimented with dogs, cats, baboons, mice, elephants—anything but men. Before the war I was assured quite seriously by the head of a well known school of dietetics that unless I ate at least 3,000 calories a day, and included meat in my diet as well, I should be either a physical wreck or dead by the time I reached forty-five. To-day I eat even less than I did then, and am fitter.

The yogis say, " If you're not hungry, why eat?" This sounds so full of commonsense, and is so simple that most people ignore it. People drink when they feel the need for liquid; not because it is one o'clock, or four, or eight. Yet, they eat at specially appointed hours, whether they feel hungry or not. Doesn't sound sensible, does it?

Sometimes I'm hungrier than at others, so I eat more. At other times I don't feel like eating, so I cut out lunch, or supper, and take only fruit juice, water or tea.

This kind of living suits me and my wife wonderfully.

They say that by the time a man reaches forty he is either his own doctor or a fool. It's amazing how many people start calling in the doctor when they reach forty, simply because they've never taken the trouble to study their own bodies. If they had, they'd not be needing doctors. Personally, I like doctors. They tell the most amusing stories, they're well read, many are accomplished in other fields, and some of them are excellent sportsmen. If I broke a leg or tumbled headfirst down an escalator, I should have no hesitation in letting a doctor go over me. But I have never needed them for flu or colds or any of the other curative processes which most of us have to go through periodically.

Probably by now you think I'm talking rubbish. Because of the unnatural conditions under which we all live, I sometimes feel under the weather for a day or so —seldom more. I know what's wrong, and it's usually my fault.

One of the main causes of disease is the sinful habit of *regular meals*. Have you ever wondered why meals are so regular when everything else is not? The weather, for instance, is not; and the seasons blow hot and cold. Yet, we ignore all this and make ourselves creatures of habit. When I was a boy I was stuffed, willy-nilly, with four " square " meals each day, whether I needed them or not, till my digestion rebelled and I fell an easy prey to disease.

Do what the yogis do, and on a lower level, what animals do. If you're not hungry, don't eat. Miss a meal; miss two meals; miss a whole day of meals and you'll feel all the better for it. It's amazing the number of meals you can miss and yet survive. Going without food rarely killed anyone. On the other hand, any number of people dig their graves with their knives and forks.

During the war, when so-called strengthening foods were scarce, the nation was fitter than at any time before, and young people were stronger, taller and heavier than at any period of our history.

It's not the quantity you eat, but the kind of food you eat, the way in which you combine it with other food and the thoroughness with which you masticate it that matters. If you eat too much, or too rapidly, you tax your digestion and ultimately weaken your whole body.

A friend who served for some years in Syria during the war told me with astonishment of massive Arabs who kept going all day on nothing but a handful of dates and figs and a little goat's milk, without exhibiting the least trace of fatigue. He added, as if in explanation, " But they're Arabs; they're used to it. It wouldn't suit us, of course!"

I've tried dozens of experiments with food—all on myself and none on dogs or monkeys—and have come to the conclusion, a view shared by men like Hindehede and Professor Chittenden, that a great deal of protein food is necessary neither for the maintenance of health nor strength. Decide by experiment just how much protein you need, and never vary it very much. Chittenden says that a person's protein intake should never vary, no matter how much hard work he does. An excess of any food, especially protein, throws an immense strain on the digestive organs and tires one physically as well as mentally.

I cannot stress too strongly the need for thorough mastication, even to the point of chewing into liquid everything you eat, before swallowing it. Chewing exercises the teeth and gums, thus keeping them healthy. It enables all carbohydrates to be thoroughly prepared for digestion before being swallowed, and it enables your body to make use of every morsel you eat.

Horace Fletcher made a fetish of thorough mastication, but in view of the enormous benefits he derived from it, one can hardly blame him. Anyone interested in the subject should buy the book outlining his experiments. They will find it absorbing.

Huge tomes have been written about the value of different foods, but if you intend getting the best out of yoga, I advise you to cut out meat. Do it by easy stages. Yoga abhors drastic measures. Even if you can't do without meat, you can gain considerable benefit from yoga, but your sensitivity will be affected, and it is this that one should desire to cultivate.

Whatever you do—don't become a crank. If you visit people who don't know that you're a vegetarian, don't shy in horror if they place meat before you. Remember; they have feelings, too. There is bound to be something else that you *can* eat and enjoy, and in any case, meat won't kill you.

Eat according to your needs. If you do hard manual work, eat to satisfy your hunger, but always rise from the table while you are able to eat and enjoy more. This is not a manual on food, and in one short chapter I do not intend to tell you all about proteins, carbohydrates, fats, vitamins and mineral salts. I could not if I would. Nor is it possible to say much about the various combinations, except that where possible make it a general rule to avoid mixing starchy foods with acid foods; or starches with foods rich in protein, because such combinations tend to overwork the digestive organs. If you are really interested, buy a book on Food Reform and learn why this is so.

Always eat wholewheat bread, and never white, adulterated, so-called *pure* bread, which is really the most emasculated bread you can buy.

Eat all your food as near the natural state as possible; fruit and fresh green vegetables uncooked, as they are, in salad form. I listen with amusement to females on the radio telling me to boil watercress and lettuce, as if fresh cress and crisp lettuces are not much tastier than anything a cook can devise. Every day throughout the land housewives stand for hours over hot stoves, cooking the goodness out of food, which when prepared, is devoured in a few minutes. Then they waste more time washing piles of greasy plates and dishes—as if there isn't enough worthwhile work to be done without making some!

Eat as varied a diet as possible, and make use of the food grown in your country. Those who live in the English countryside have a variety of fresh foods on their very doorsteps; herbs such as town dwellers seldom see. Fields and hedges are rich with them: sorrel, dandelion and nettle, to name a few; free for the picking. The woods and fields are filled with mushrooms and *other fungi*, such as shaggy caps, champignons and beletus, which when cooked add a piquancy to all dishes.

Yoga writings lay it down that indigenous foods should be eaten, as Nature has meant them for the people of the country in which they are found. Nature knows better than most of us think. The Scots thrive on oats; the Irish on potatoes; and the English on rich cheeses that cannot be bettered—Cheddar, Wensleydale and rich, ripe Stilton. In India they thrive on lentils and wholemeal, unleavened bread; or lentils and rice. In Java, rice and fish; in China, soya beans and rice. In all warm countries much fruit and sour milk is eaten by those who can afford to buy it. In the East they call such milk *tyre;* in South-Eastern Europe, *yogourt.*

The best food in the world is simple food. It is tastiest when you're hungry. And nothing makes one hungrier than hard work and meals well spaced out.

Enjoyment of food has a great deal to do with health. Enjoy all you eat and it will do you good. There is something wrong either with you or your food if you have to spatter it with sauces and chutneys.

A word about dried fruits. They contain a great deal of energy-producing natural sugar which is easily assimilated, they are rich in mineral salts. Get your energy from such sources rather than from refined white sugar and golden syrup. Every kind of dried fruit is good: raisins, sultanas, figs, olives, peaches, apples, nectarines, preserved fruits, dried bananas.

I've often been asked how much a person should drink —a foolish question. Drink according to your wants, and drink freely. Don't drink during meals. If you're really thirsty, nothing quenches the thirst so satisfyingly as pure water, whether from a spring or a tap. In civilised countries a great deal of brewed liquid must be taken unless you wish to be dubbed a crank. Neither tea nor coffee is as harmful as it is made out to be. People claim that coffee is pernicious because it contains a drug called caffeine; but no one points out that it contains at least 17 other drugs. Tea contains tannin; rhubarb leaves are poisonous; inside peach stones there is strychnine; tomatoes contain oxalic acid, and so on. Almost every food we eat contains some substance that is injurious if taken in excess. Lettuce, for example, contains laudanum.

I drink a good deal of very weak tea without sugar; sometimes without milk, but with lemon and sugar. I am sure it does me no harm, and when not actually thirsty, it is more refreshing and palatable than plain water. I like a cup of good strong coffee after lunch, and am certain that it has no adverse effect. There is nothing in yoga teachings about either tea or coffee, for neither beverage was known when yoga was being developed.

Those who wish to benefit from yoga are asked to abstain from all alcoholic drinks. But yoga is a cult of moderation, and I feel that an occasional glass of wine or beer can do little harm. Spirits, on the other hand, are harmful, and I do not advise them, except in emergencies; such as a glass of brandy after an accident.

There are, however, numerous delicious pure fruit drinks which I much prefer to alcoholic beverages: apple, grape, grape-fruit, orange, lemon, pineapple and other fresh juices. Even the juices of carrots and other vegetables. They are palatable, and much better for you than wine. On the other hand, a glass of wine on some festive occasion never did anyone a ha'porth of harm.

Far worse than an occasional glass of wine is the crime of gluttony. Often a person who would not disgrace himself by drinking too much, thinks nothing of gorging till he feels ill. Gluttony is a crime against good taste and the man who hides his fat stomach under a well cut waist-coat should be ashamed of himself.

Cut out stimulating foods, such as salt, pepper, chutneys, pickles and foods that tend to constipate, like white bread.

Yoga advises one not to eat between meals. At least four hours must elapse between one meal and the next; if possible, longer. If you eat four *square* meals, arrange to do without one; if three, cut them down to two. Even one good meal a day is an excellent idea; the meal to be eaten after work.

In everything you do, use your commonsense. Eat according to your requirements. Eat when hungry. Eat natural foods in preference to proprietary articles. Eat raw food in preference to cooked. Rise from the table when you can still go on eating.

I am afraid I am fussy about my food. I don't eat anything. I'm careful what I put inside my mouth. My stomach is not a dust-bin. Why should it be otherwise? Why should I treat my stomach differently from the rest of my body? I am careful about the clothes I wear, the books I read, the music I listen to, the friends I invite to my home, and the kind of language I use. I don't as a rule read pornographic literature or use the language attributed to a Billingsgate fish porter (during the war I was stationed in Fish Street Hill, Billingsgate, and did not hear a single swear word!), so why should I be indiscriminate about my food? My stomach and I are on excellent terms. Why should I insult it?

CHAPTER V

Yoga Breathing

THE principles on which yoga breathing are based are so sound that those who evolved the system must have had a considerable knowledge of the structure of the lungs and the mechanics of breathing. We know now that the surgeons of Ancient India were amazingly skilled; that they worked with some 150 kinds of instruments and performed abdominal operations and operations in rhinology, which were not again attempted until late in the nineteenth century, after the discovery and use of anæsthetics.

In order to understand yoga methods of breathing one must have at least an elementary knowledge of the structure of the lungs. In talks with people devoid of medical knowledge I find that they imagine that the lungs are like bags which inflate and deflate as we breathe in and out. They talk about them as bellows, and as bellows they become fixed in the mind. The lungs are encased in the thorax, with the ribs acting as a protecting cage. The heart lies midway between.

The function of the lungs is not to puff in and out like a pair of bellows, but to interchange the gases inside the body with the gases of the atmosphere. The lungs consist of a spongy, elastic substance containing minute air sacs, and when you take a deep breath the air is sucked down your windpipe into these sacs.

About one fifth of the atmosphere consists of oxygen which is absorbed, through these air sacs, by the red cells, and carbon-dioxide is thrown out by the air sacs, so that when you breathe out you get rid of this poison.

The lungs can be likened to sponges rather than bellows, though even this analogy is not quite correct.

Oxygen, one only of the constituents of life, is needed for absorbing your food. Everything that you eat is burnt inside your body by a chemical process, just as coal is burnt in a grate. Coal cannot burn if there is no oxygen in the atmosphere; likewise, your food cannot be consumed without oxygen, so unless you have it you will die fairly quickly.

But though oxygen is a most important constituent of air, there are other vital properties in the atmosphere. It is a gas consisting of 77 parts of nitrogen, 23 of oxygen, a trace of carbon-dioxide, ammonia, argon, nitrates, organic matter, and water vapour. And, in large cities and industrial districts, air is generously mixed with coal dust, brick dust, hair, splinters of wood, pollen, injurious substances, poisonous gases and other matter. If sucked into the lungs in large quantities, these impurities clog the tiny air sacs or alveoli as they are termed, and render the act of respiration difficult and painful.

Take a sponge and keep on squeezing it and letting it out alternately in thick muddy water, and you will find that in time the spaces in the sponge become clogged, and fresh water is needed to cleanse it. The sponge you use for cleaning your car soon gets clogged with oil and dirt, which hardens until it is impossible to clean it. In the end you get a new sponge. Lungs are not quite like sponges, for they are living organs with a circulatory system of their own, and have the capacity to heal and repair themselves, like other parts of the body. But they can be destroyed if you make them breathe air that is thick with impurities for long periods on end.

Don't imagine that correct breathing is natural. Man has to learn the art of living. He has to learn how to stand, to sit, walk, use his muscles, breathe and eat. There is a wrong and a right way for most things, and it is astonishing how few do the right thing automatically. Those who do not sit properly are likely to develop curvature of the spine. If you persistently walk badly or wear the wrong footwear, fallen arches or bunions will result. Use your muscles wrongly and you will develop a lop-sided frame or become muscle bound. Eat the wrong foods and a hundred complaints will follow; think the wrong thoughts and you can turn yourself into a monster.

Live in a foul atmosphere and breathe wrongly and you will pay the penalty. Man was given intelligence and powers of observation, and he was meant to use them.

In order to make use of all the beneficial particles in the atmosphere—not only the oxygen needed for burning your food—breathing must be done in four stages—not two—as most physical culture systems advise.

The four stages of yoga breathing are: suspension, inhalation, retention, exhalation.

But the first requisite for healthy living is the right atmosphere. In Britain, an island swept by cleansing breezes, almost anywhere in the country is healthy, though the ideal location is about 500-1,000 feet above sea level.

Man was never meant to eke out his existence in huge industrial towns, and if he in his folly has seen fit to create them, he must suffer the consequences of the monsters he has created.

All sane men will, if circumstances permit, live in the country or by the sea. For centuries soot and smoke have been the bane of civilised men. Even Horace inveighed against atmospheric pollution, for in Ode III, 6, he says: (Cudworth's translation)

" On thee will rest thy father's stain,
    Though guiltless, Roman, till thou put
    In order shrine and mouldering fane,
    And statue grimed with dingy soot."

The danger of fetid and impure air is a very real one. Howes writes in the year 1631: " Within 30 years last the nice dames of London would not come into any house or room where sea coales were burned, nor willingly eat of the meat that was either sod or roasted with sea coale fire."

John Evelyn, too, fulminates against the noxious fumes thrown into the atmosphere by coal. " That men whose very being is Aer, should not breathe it freely when they may, but condemn themselves to this misery . . . is strange stupidity. It is this horrid Smoake which obscures our Churches, and makes our Palaces look old, which fouls our Clothes, and corrupts the Waters . . . with its black and tenacious quality, spots and contaminates whatever is exposed to it."

The atmospheric pollution of our cities costs us thousands of lives and millions of pounds each year. The heaviest sootfall in the world is, fortunately, not in Britain, but over Woods Run, Pittsburg, and is 2,736 tons to every square mile! London's worst pollution was at Golden Lane: 644 tons to the square mile. But the air over English industrial cities is so foul that the smoke hanging over them has been observed 350 miles out at sea.

Often, when London or Manchester is hidden in a pall of smoke, airmen fly above the foul blanket in brilliant sunshine. Recently, when in the interests of science some measurements were taken, it was found that on a dull winter's day Holt Town, Manchester, obtained only 39.1 per cent. of daylight!

Enough facts and figures about the harmful effects of smoke and dirt could be given to fill a large volume, but it will suffice if I add that during one week in December, when there was no fog in Manchester, the deaths from respiratory diseases was only 137; but a few days later, when fog enveloped the city, deaths from the same causes rose to 592, and it has since been found that there is always a big increase in such deaths during fog.

The world seems to have gone mad. Authorities in every country are willing to pour out thousands of millions of pounds on weapons to wipe each other out, when a millionth of such sums will fill empty stomachs, eradicate slums, and give us towns fit to live in. Instead of living in garden cities, most of us live in huge industrial octopi, amid dust, dirt and noise.

Yoga breathing, if practised regularly, can counteract many of the deleterious effects of atmospheric pollution. It is known as Pranayama; *prana* means *breath*, and *ayama, pause*. Literally Pranayama means breathing and pausing. And that is just what most yoga breathing is: pause, inhale; pause, exhale. All sorts of mystical interpretations have been placed on the word, but it means just that.

For centuries yogis have known the value of fresh air, even when in Europe it was regarded with intense suspicion, and people slept behind hermetically sealed doors in vast canopied beds to keep out the ill vapours and humours of winter. Such superstitions still exist and there are thousands of country people who close their windows and draw curtains when they retire for the night. There are still millions who think that " night air " is harmful, and because people will not breathe freely respiratory diseases are common throughout Europe. During the war the incidence of T-B in the Navy—because of crowded conditions and lack of air space—was appalling. Almost as many ratings went down with diseases of the lungs as with wounds.

Live in a well ventilated house or flat, breathe freely, and you need never fear lung diseases.

Learn to breathe scientifically, and you will *cure* many diseases, despite all that the doctors can do.

Cold water, fresh air and proper breathing would empty more hospital wards than the latest appliances of medical science, especially if the rations of the patients were cut down by half.

Tubercolosis does not afflict only civilised persons or those who live in cities. Curiously enough, it used to be prevalent among German, Austrian and Russian shepherds, who despite an outdoor existence during the day, shut themselves up at night in small wooden boxes about 8 ft. by 4 ft. by 6 ft. These boxes were built for warmth and had no windows, so for seven or eight hours that same azotised fetid air was breathed.

In his excellent work on " Yoga," Dr. K. T. Behanan outlines the results of experiments carried out on breathing at Yale University. He states that taking normal breathing as a basis, it was found that the yoga breathing exercise *ujjayi* increased oxygen consumption by 24.4 per cent., *bhastrika* by 18.5 per cent., and *kapalabhati* by 12 per cent. These experiments merely took into consideration oxygen consumption, whereby food is more easily burned and digestion hastened. The yogis apparently knew this without such experiments and that is why they claim that their type of breathing assists the unnaturally thin to put on healthy flesh.

But there are other constituents in the atmosphere, which if breathed not only into the lungs, but *mentally,* throughout the body, endow it with powers to get rid of disease and increase its powers of resistance.

In India, since time immemorial, air has been considered to have some nutritive value, and an excursion into the open is known as *Howa khana*—eating air. The yogis say that there is a constituent of air—so far not isolated—which they call *Prana* and sometimes *Akasha,* which if imbibed into the system, increases health and vitality. Who knows? There is so much in yoga that has been endorsed by doctors and scientists that within the next few years they might pinpoint this elusive element.

No one doubts that there is illimitable power in the atmosphere. The atom bomb hurled on Hiroshima was not much larger than a football, but its power was tremendous. In his book *The Ether of Space* Sir Oliver Lodge writes: " The density of Ether is something like 50,000 times that of platinum, and the amount of ethereal energy in every cubic millimentre of space is equal to that of a one million horse-power power station working continuously for forty million years."

Few of us possess the knowledge to question this statement, but if all that power is contained in space, it is not unlikely that certain kinds of breathing can make use of some of it. The claims of yoga are not theoretical. They are based on results. Those who have tried them have gained health and vitality; many claim spiritual elevation as well, but the yogis say that body, mind and spirit are merely different forms of the same thing. All have a common source.

Lack of fresh air affects your heart, dulls your mind and makes you lethargic. All these facts are known to adults who deliberately starve themselves of air and so poison themselves. Breathing affects your heart, that vigorous organ which it is so difficult to overwork. The more efficiently you breathe, the longer and more strongly your heart will pump, and the longer you should live. In a single day your heart, pumping at the average rate of 72 beats a minute, pulsates no fewer than 103,680 times, pumps 2,500 gallons of blood, and does as much work as will raise 130 tons to a height of one foot. All the blood in your body passes through your heart every three minutes. Your heart never stops work.

It is an extremely tough organ and hard to wear out; but so badly do some people ill treat it that hundreds of thousands suffer from heart complaints. If you learn how to breathe the right way, however, your heart will respond till eventually it stops functioning from sheer old age.

The yogis say that breath is both positive as well as negative, and that the breath flowing into the right nostril is *hot,* and known as the Sun breath or *Pingala;* that through the left nostril is cold and known as the Moon breath or *Ida.* In short, that the breath flowing through the right nostril produces heat, and that through the left cooling effects.

Scientists may say " Stuff and nonsense!" but in my extremely limited way I have found that yoga breathing has brought results that no other form of physical culture or medical teaching has achieved. To be able to recline in a cold bath in mid-winter and feel better for it, is, I maintain, a positive result. I wonder whether the time will come when I can, from choice, walk abroad in winter in just trousers, shirt and jacket, without a top coat?

If you breathe properly all the time, each nostril automatically and alternately does the main portion of work for one hour and fifty minutes; but I am not a master of yoga and my breath does not alternate with such regularity, which is the sign of perfect health.

The breathing system is more closely linked with the nervous system than we imagine, and if you breathe through one nostril *only*, for more than 24 hours at a stretch, it is a sign that some form of physical breakdown is near and that the body needs a complete rest, if only for a day or two. If one nostril is completely blocked for two or three days, a serious breakdown is imminent.

This is a sure sign that *Prana*—the life principle—is affected.

When I was young I remember having a severe cold during which both nostrils were completely blocked and I was forced to breathe through my mouth. My father was holding a metaphysical discussion with one of his yogi friends, who noticed my snuffling efforts. He called me over, took my little cricket bat, placed the handle on the ground and the bottom of the bat under my right armpit. " Press down," he directed, and in about a minute my *left* nostril was quite free! He then made me repeat the trick under the other arm, and my right nostril became free. Since then I have often adopted this method of freeing a blocked nostril, or changing the flow of my breath. You can use a crutch, the back of a chair—anything over which an arm can be placed, and which which will press on the nerves under your arm. If there is nothing else to hand, sit on the floor, crook one knee, place an armpit over the kneecap, and press. The opposite nostril will become free.

Yoga is the cult of moderation. Avoid extremes. Yoga breathing must always be practised in such a way that strain is never placed on any part of the body. Never hold your breath till it becomes an effort; never exhale or pause without breathing till you feel giddy. But gradually, as you do the exercises, your powers will increase.

The main difference between western breathing and yoga breathing is the *pause*. Western schools insist on deep, rhythmic breathing. The idea of holding the breath for minutes at a time horrifies them. But then, they don't regard air as a food; something to be taken into the body and absorbed into the blood, as yogis do.

By the exercise of will power, concentration and *imagination* yogis believe that they take something from the air; extract some vital elixir which we do not believe exists. Therein lies the difference.

Don't spurn the use of imagination. It is not merely something that poets and lovers make use of, but a very real force for producing health, happiness and success.

CHAPTER VI

The Secret of Eternal Youth

FEW men, even among the very needy, will, unless they are temporarily unhinged, try to take their own lives. Even those who commit suicide while apparently in full possession of their faculties, do so only when on the brink of despair, or because they have experienced such misfortune or disappointment that life for the moment seems purposeless and futile. They are, for the time, abnormal.

Instinctively, the normal man wants to continue on this planet, and even those who lose no opportunity of proclaiming their lack of interest in the future, hop hurriedly enough out of the way of oncoming vehicles. The instinct of self-preservation is strong. More than that; most people have a secret desire for immortality, which is one reason why the theory of life in the hereafter is so acceptable. Few of us can conceive a future in which we shall not exist. We resent the encroachment of age, and like to feel that when we die and our bodies are interred, something of us will continue. We know that no material part can continue to live on, so we talk about the immortality of the soul.

Our first battle is against old age. In that we have won many minor skirmishes. Our second is against death. In this ambitious struggle we have made comparatively little headway, so far. But this we do know, and it gives us comfort; most men die before half their normal span is done.

The tortoise, the whale and the carp have all mastered a secret that has so far eluded Man. They continue for centuries. Why can't we?

I believe, with the yogis, that there is no such thing as "natural death." Death is unnatural, and it is inevitable only because Man has lost the secret of eternal life. I have spoken with yogis who seemed to be able to control some of the laws of nature, and they have told me that anyone who masters yoga thoroughly can live on indefinitely; that some yogis have lived for centuries and have released themselves from their bodies only when their purpose on earth is accomplished, and when they are ready for a higher stage of evolution. Whatever the truth of this, I am positive that Man was meant to live a good deal longer than seventy years, which is the normal span of life in this country. A century ago the normal span was thirty; in India to-day it is 23.

By working a limited number of hours, eating the right foods and taking enough rest, we have managed to increase our span of life. One day the average span of life in India will be 70; by that time our conditions should be even better and the average span perhaps 100. Plutarch wrote that the Ancient Britons *began to grow old* at 125, so the normal span of life must then have been from 150 to 200.

If this seems fantastic, let us see how long the lower animals live. The duration of growth of the dog, cat, ox, horse and camel are 2, 1.5, 4, 5 and 8 years respectively; and they lived eventually to 10-15, 8-10, 20, 20-30 and 40 years. Man completes his full growth between 20-25, and according to this, should live to about 150 years. Exceptional men should live to 200.

I maintain that if a man dies before the age of 150 he is killed by " civilising influences;" overwork, illness, worry, unfavourable environment or lack of hygiene.

To me the wonder of it is that men live as long as they do. Almost as soon as we are out of the cradle we begin flaunting the rules of right living in the most alarming way. Knowingly we eat and drink a good deal that disagrees with us. We keep late hours, work too long and too hard under bad conditions, and *allow ourselves to suffer* all sorts of harmful physical and emotional stresses. In spite of the fact that we hanker after life, we do our utmost to terminate the life span.

From time immemorial men have tried to probe the secret of immortality; failing this, they have tried to preserve the spark of life indefinitely. There have always been men who believed that with proper attention the body can repair and preserve itself for hundreds of years.

It is possible for men to live for centuries, provided they know how. I once spoke with a yogi who described events which must have taken place in the sixteenth century. He remembered the early days of the John Company (East India Company) and the end of Moghul rule. He was an old man in years during the Napoleonic Wars, and yet there was something perennially youthful about him. His case, though exceptional, is by no means incredible.

There are scores of cases of people other than yogis who have lived useful lives for two or three times the normal span. Mere longevity is, in my opinion, of little value— despite the Chinese belief that old age in itself is meritorious —unless one enjoys good health, is active, and continues a useful and interesting life. Merely to exist like a cabbage, a burden and a trial to everyone round you, is worse than death.

One does not have to go back to Methuselah's time to find men and women who have exceeded 150 years on this planet. The most outstanding authenticated case is that of Take Nouchi, a Japanese prime minister, whose face is engraved on the one-yen bank notes. He was born in 3 A.D. and died in the year 311. He became prime minister at the age of 32 and held office for 276 years. Another ancient was Li Chung Yun, who, according to official records vouched for by Professor Wu-Chung-Cheih, Dean of Chang-Tu University, was born in 1677, in the province of Szechuen. In 1827 the Chinese government sent Li their official felicitations for his 150th birthday, and again in 1877 he was congratulated on reaching his 200th year. For all I know, Li Chung Yun may still be alive, though 1932 was the last occasion on which I still heard of him. He was then 255, had married and outlived 23 wives, and was wed at the time to a mere infant of some sixty years.

The most celebrated centenarian in Europe was undoubtedly the almost legendary Count St. Germain. Madam de Gergy, wife of the French ambassador, records that he appeared at a carnival in Venice in 1710 wearing diamonds, each worth a thousand guineas, as buttons on his coat. He then looked about fifty. Various eminent men, Horace Walpole among them, met St. Germain in the next hundred years, and each writes that he looked no more than an active and well preserved fifty. The last occasion was in 1820. St. Germain, it was rumoured, had wrested some of the secrets of eternal youth. Why he was not seen after 1820 no one knows, but men say that he had lived 500 years.

His was not a fully authenticated case, but there are many carefully checked records of people who have lived 150 years or more. Katherine Fitzgerald, Countess of Desmond, would undoubtedly have exceeded this had she not climbed a tree at the age of 140 and died from the resulting fall. Most people relinquish such activities more than 100 years earlier, but she was strong and active enough to think nothing of walking ten miles a day, several times each week. Another old crone was La Anciana Martina Gomez, of Cuba, who died at 153 and to the very end ate with her own teeth and read the news-papers without the aid of spectacles.

We have our own Thomas Parr, who was hale and hearty on good Shropshire ale and bread and cheese for 152 years, and looked like going on indefinitely till he was taken to London at the King's wish, where rich feeding and riotous living made an end to him. Nor, by all accounts, was Parr an anchorite, for he was courting when 115 and married his last wife at 122, and till the day of his death had an eye for a well turned leg. Henry Jenkins was another Englishman who enjoyed a long, full life, for he died at 169.

The oldest European I've seen was Zaro Agha, the aged Turk, who had his picture taken dandling a chorus girl on his knee. He was brought to London as a raree show, then whisked over to America—and that, I should imagine, was the end of him. He claimed to be 162.

Not long ago the newspapers recorded the death of Joseph Gurrington, who was born in Norway in 1797; he married several times and left one son aged 103, and another aged nine. Before the war a man named Jonas Kursonia, of Kaunas, Lithuania, was driving a plough on his farm at the age of 117; a peasant named Shapkovsky, in the village of Laty, near Sukhum, still went about his labours, youthful and virile at 140. His third wife was 82 and his youngest daughter 26. The same year—1926 —a woman named Martsiana Maliarevich, living in Novoborisov, walked 13 miles to register her vote. She was 130. Ten years later a man named Michael Moor walked into the offices of the Manchester Relief Committee to demand a pension, for he thought his age entitled him to one. His birth record showed him to be 123.

People can be fit at almost any age. They can earn a living at well over a hundred. The newspapers have been packed with articles about that remarkable man, Theodore C. Taylor, Yorkshire mill owner, who still runs his business at a hundred. He must be a very fine man, indeed, but no better than a Senora Ramirez, aged 113, of Mexico City, who just before the war was earning a living as a laundress. The government offered her a house and pension, but she scorned them, saying that she was still strong and active.

The subject of perennial youth intrigues me. If I cannot be young for ever, I should at least like to be fit and active as long as I live. When I can no longer get about easily, enjoy good food, congenial company, books and music, or play outdoor games, I should like to leave this world. The idea of becoming a burden to people is abhorrent to me. I have seen too many old people who merely exist; whose relatives are relieved when they die. That seems to me to be a dreadful fate.

For the last thirty years I have not felt a single day older, except for a brief period during the war, when the lack of fresh food and the strain of war was getting us all down. I now feel fitter and stronger than I did thirty years ago, and when I look around me and see men 20 years younger giving up sport and looking forward to the day they will retire and prod gently in their gardens, I feel that there is something wrong with their mental attitude.

The idea of a retirement pension at 65 or 70 is admirable, but with it also goes the idea that one is *OLD* at 65. Seventy should be middle age. And middle age should last till one is 125. A man gains experience for 20 or 30 years, and just when he is really worth something and is willing to work hard, his employers turn him out to grass. They should make use of his knowledge and experience, give him shorter hours, if necessary, or less physical work, but not throw him aside. Millions of pounds worth of brain power is thus wasted each year.

When is a man old? The yogis say that old age is a state of mind. The minute you feel old, you *are* old. To use a colloquialism, " You've had it." During the war I lectured with a young fellow of thirty. He looked fifty and went about as if he was a patriarch of ninety. Already he was old, and I expect to read his obituary in *The Times* almost any day. His ambition was to amass enough to give him a small income so that he could retire to a cottage in some remote area of East Anglia to read John Donne, and Skelton and Suckling and Crashaw for the rest of his life.

One never hears of a yogi " retiring." The word has as little meaning as " impossible " had for Napoleon, of " defeat " for Queen Victoria.

If Winston Churchill had been retired at 65, he would not have done his best work. Nor would Lloyd George. Wagner would not have composed " Parsifal," nor

Rembrandt, nor Franz Hals, nor Corot some of their loveliest works. Victor Hugo, Titian, Michael Angelo—all produced excellent work when over 70. Goethe wrote the second part of *Faust* at 82, Titian was 95 when he finished *Christ Crowned With Thorns* and *The Battle of Lepanto* when he was 98, Tennyson wrote *Crossing of the Bar* when 83, Verdi wrote four operas after 73, Franklin helped frame the American Constitution after 80, and Justice Holmes was still making important Supreme Court decisions at 90. Shaw at 94 was as witty and vitriolic as ever, and working on a new play.

I could continue with my list of really old men who are mentally active and produce good work. If one is fit, physical activity, too, can be carried on far longer than it normally is. A man named Sullivan of Og Vale, Glamorgan, is still playing cricket at 94; Charlie Hart, in 1950, raced a coach and four from Windsor to Twickenham at 85, for a ten-pound bet, incidentally, winning; Christian Almer, aged 90, and his wife aged 92 celebrated their diamond wedding by climbing Wetterhorn, which is 12,166 feet; and in 1937 a Japanese named Toichiro Itoh led a party of climbers to the top of 12,390-foot Fujiyama to celebrate his 109th birthday.

I could write a book about the extraordinary mental and athletic feats of old people, but shall content myself with these few facts to show that no one should imagine that he is more than middle aged before he gets to 100. If he feels old at 65, then something is wrong with his way of living.

I was reading a statement by Dr. Marie Stopes, who said recently, " I am 26. I have been 26 for the last 30 years, and I intend remaining 26 for many more. I hope to live till I'm 140." Lord Chief Justice Hewart said that " middle age is a little farther than a man had got."

Both these people had the yoga idea—to feel as old as you are, not as old as the calendar tells you.

I think I have shown conclusively that a great many people outlive the normal span by as much as thirty or forty years, and a few have continued for more than double that span.

What is the secret of keeping young? Is there any one magic formula; some elixir that can be swallowed, which rejuvenates the whole body? The ancients firmly believed that there was, but I don't think so. I have pored over many books dealing with old age and everlasting youth, and I am sure that there is no substance that can be imbibed that will make the body go on for ever, or even keep old age at bay for a hundred years more than the normal span. Some years ago a manuscript written in the time of Emperor Chin Ize Wang, who sat on the Dragon Throne of China 5,000 years ago, was unearthed and translated by Professor Anthony Graeme. This manuscript bears out Darwin's Theory of the Origin of Species, which was formulated thousands of years before Darwin, for it says, " From the plants life passed into fantastic creatures that were born of the slime of waters; then, through a series of different shapes and animals, it came to Man." The manuscript refers to certain juices, which if taken, would increase the length of life. One mentioned is the cypress, which is poisonous, so it is probable that this juice was blended with others. But, whatever the elixir was, it could not have prolonged life indefinitely, otherwise the writer would have been alive to-day.

I have interviewed dozens of centenarians, and their recipes for longevity are both confusing as well as contradictory. For instance, Mrs. Johanna O'Connor, of MacGillicuddy Reeks, in Ireland, claims that plain food, plenty of punch, wine, stout and pipe smoking were responsible for her good health at 110. Mrs. Anna Donoghue, of Carrignavar, Co. Cork, who is but a year or two younger, attributes her health to the fact that she has never smoked and is a life-long teetotaller. William Green of Market Harborough, another centenarian, attributes his remarkable health to live frogs. " I swallow them alive, and while I continue to eat them I shall not have an ailment."

I find that an important, though not essential factor, is heredity. If you have a good start you are likely to live long, though a good start can be nullified by gross living and indolence. Thomas Parr was 153, his son 113, his grandson 109, and his great-grandson 101—all very old men, but in a descending scale.

Most of these old people were middle aged at a time when food was eaten rough, and in its natural state—when bread, for instance, was coarser than it is; when motor travel had yet to become a curse and men used their legs for locomotion, and when all but a few of the privileged classes earned their keep by manual labour.

In my opinion there is no magic formula for long life. The rules are the same, roughly, as those the yogis laid down centuries ago. Breathe plenty of fresh air. Eat food that is as near its natural state as possible; food that you must use your teeth to tear and chew, and which has not had all the natural goodness boiled out of it. Maintain your physical activity, whether by housework, by manual labour or by set physical exercises, in order to keep the blood circulating briskly and keep the limbs from becoming set. And finally maintain your interest in the world around you; whether by study, or mixing with people, or merely by good natured gossip.

The last census revealed some interesting facts about centenarians. There were 3,960 persons above the age of 100 in the United States, but 3,139 in a much smaller and less populated country, like Bulgaria. Of these only 14 had ever visited a doctor, one third were non-smokers, and nearly all drank some kind of liquor in moderation. The Bulgarian diet consists mainly of vegetables, fruit, cheese, sour milk and rough bread.

Britain had 145 centenarians, Spain 355, and the Irish Free State, with its tiny population, 116. One fact revealed was that good wine, taken in moderation, is not, apparently harmful. The people of Chailly, C'ote d'Or, in the heart of the French wine country, for instance, live longer than elsewhere in France. And in that department more wine is drunk than elsewhere.

An important ingredient of old age is happiness. I am convinced that it is the most important of all. A study of yoga shows that a contented mind is the most important factor in longevity, and a study of yoga will show one how to achieve this. But the body must first be developed into such a state of fitness that you can ignore it and concentrate on the mind. Bodily fitness depends largely upon the food one eats, but once fitness and mental control are achieved, a man may eat almost anything and keep fit. So the yogis say.

How often does one see men who ignore all the rules of health and yet retain robust health; how often do we meet cranks who make a life-long study of health, but never achieve a single day of it?

Before the war the people of Japan were prosperous and contented. According to their ideas they lived well. There was no unemployment. Japanese goods captured every market they invaded. Japan had the highest standard of literacy in the world, and more books per head were read there than in either Britain or the United States. In Tokio alone there were 114 centenarians, who in 1939 were given prizes by a local newspaper.

Most of them were still at work. The youngest was 103, a school teacher still employed by the state! In Britain his useful span would have been ended forty years earlier, but in Japan he was allowed to accumulate and pour out wisdom.

The diet of all these old people was investigated and found to consist mainly of rice, fish and pickles; rice, which according to western dieteticians contains too much starch, fish which has little or no protein, and pickles, a surfeit of which causes stomach ulcers and makes for an early grave. But these people were content with the régime under which they lived; they had enough food and money, no fear of the future, and most of them had numerous interests. *Their minds were at peace.*

I am convinced that an active, interested and peaceful mind is most important. My father's mother was a God-fearing soul, who never in her life touched liquor, ate sparingly and achieved mental happiness by reading the family Bible daily. She lived to 98. My mother's father lived a wild and vigorous life. The wild oats he sowed would have fed the entire county of Cork, where he lived. Seldom a day passed without whisky oozing from his pores. But he, too, had a happy life, and lived to 98.

The yogis live a full life. Europeans imagine that they spend all their time sitting naked on mountain slopes. They do nothing of the sort.

The life of a yogi is spent in doing good works unassumingly; in helping people; in the service of mankind. Such time as he has to himself he spends either in discussion or trying to fathom the nature of existence. He travels from village to village studying human nature, coming into contact with thousands, learning their problems and doing what he can to help them. Such power as he develops he uses for the benefit of mankind.

Those who give constantly of themselves know what an exhausting process this is, so from time to time the yogi retires to the mountains, or into some remote spot to rest and relax and regenerate his body, and to draw upon the illimitable reserves of Nature.

The ancients in India were wiser than we imagine. They were meticulous observers belonging to the empirical school of philosophers. As a result of their observations they erected the system we now call Yoga. Nothing that they teach is entirely theoretical. Everything has an ultimate practical value.

Their system contains breathing exercises and *asanas* which, if practised with the rest of their philosophy, are calculated to cure disease and prolong youth.

I have often been asked, " Which yoga exercise will develop bodily heat?" or " Which will make one cool in summer?" or " What must I do to ward off old age?"

Every part of their system is interdependent upon the others. But there are some that help the body to achieve certain effects, *but only if practised with the rest.* The breathing exercise known as *Sitkari* helps to make the body cool, just as *Suryabheda* helps to increase bodily temperature, and *Bhastrika* maintains the body at an even temperature. There are many others, both breathing as well as *asanas* which are valuable in the prevention and cure of specific diseases. But all these will fail if used alone and to the exclusion of others. Many students fail to realise this, concentrate on one or more, and become extremely disappointed with the study, which like every other gives just as much as you put into it.

The intelligent student gains more than one who does not study the effects of yoga-practise on his own body.

Long before Harvey discovered that Man had a blood circulation, the yogis must have known it, for by means of mind, nerve and breath control they could control the pumping of the heart and the beat of the pulse. In the same way, they realised long before Meckel touched upon the idea in 1806, or Schiff, working in Geneva experimented with the thyroid gland, that certain tiny areas of the body —they did not know all about them—controlled growth, intelligence as well as specific functions, and they devised exercises for strengthening and developing these areas.

They could not cure cretinism, nor could they control the pituitary, but they knew that certain organs secreted vital fluids and substances, which enables the body to renew itself and slow down metabolism, and this enables Man to live longer.

It is doubtful whether we shall ever learn how the yogis came to their conclusions, for their teachings were passed down by word of mouth. In India there seems to be no written record of their very earliest work. If any such records exist, they will be found in the remote monasteries of Tibet, the home of the Tantrik scholars.

Almost all systems of western physical culture have adopted one or more yoga exercises. Ling based his system on that of the Ancient Greeks, and on a somewhat superficial study of yoga. All Muller's skin-rubbing and sun therapy is pure yoga, whether he knew it or not. Maxalding, which is Max Sick's system, contains numerous exercises, particularly the *abdominal roll*, and the *isolation of the rectus abdominum*, which are nothing but elementary forms of the *bandhas*. But obviously Max Sick did not know what the *bandhas* were meant to achieve, and in his system the exercises are not followed to their logical conclusion.

CHAPTER VII

The Value of Sound Sleep

I ENJOY sleep so much and awake so refreshed that I find it difficult to realise that thousands lie awake most of the night, tossing and turning, and when eventually they crawl from their beds they do so bleary-eyed and with imprecations and moans. For a considerable time after waking they are scarcely human, and snap and snarl if spoken to. If thoroughly refreshed you should awake so mentally alert that you could tackle a mathematical problem five minutes after opening your eyes.

Sleep I consider not only one of the necessities of life, but a most enjoyable luxury.

As with food and exercise, I've experimented a good deal with sleep. I've tried to do without it, and I've tried to prolong it unduly, and I know the effect that any particular period of sleep will have on me. Seven or eight hours are sufficient for my needs. I can get along with six without impairing my efficiency, but nine are a trifle too much, except on rare occasions. Sleep is an individual matter, and as in other things, you can school your body to do with more or less sleep.

There is no hard and fast rule about sleeping. Some like to retire fairly early and rise at cock-crow; others are at their best at midnight, but are later-risers.

Sleep is more important than food. You will die if deprived of air for ten minutes, of water for a week, and of sleep for ten days. Men have gone without food for about three months and not only survived, but felt better for the rest they have given their stomachs. One of the most refined of Chinese tortures was to keep a victim awake for days on end, till he went mad. Apparently in America and elsewhere the police inflict this type of torture on prisoners from whom they desire to extort confessions. Bright lights are focused on their eyes till sleep is impossible and from sheer desperation the prisoner is willing to sign his name to any confession so long as he is allowed to sleep.

What is it that causes us to feel sleepy at regular intervals? What causes us to yawn, our eyelids to droop and burn, and our heads to nod?

The yogis say that there are periods during every 24 hours when we lose our normal sense, and when acts which would normally seem reprehensible appear perfectly ethical. And that it is during this period that Nature sends us to sleep as a safeguard. They say that the *tendency* of the blood to become acid must be neutralised, and it is during sleep that the alkalinising process takes place.

This is amazingly in keeping with modern ideas, for according to yoga, we tend to commit crimes when the body is unhealthy; and according to psychologists, criminals are really sick people. Incidentally, the blood never becomes acid, otherwise we should die.

Sleep is also a matter of temperature adjustment. Nature is constantly seeking to maintain a balance between Pingala, the warm currents breathed into the body; and Ida, the cool currents, and when sleep overtakes one, Ida has reached its maximum strength.

The body is a mass of vibrations. The so-called solid portions, the bones and flesh are merely vibrations at a different rate. When the wave lengths change, as after death, the composition of the flesh changes, too, and is ultimately decomposed into gaseous matter.

This theory of vibrations is strangely in keeping with one put forward by Sir Oliver Lodge, who stated that a healthy, living cell has certain maximum and minimum vibrations, and when the cells are loaded with fatigue poisons, their vibrations alter and they become temporarily unhealthy, and the whole process of metabolism slows down until one naturally falls into the coma we call sleep. During this period the lungs, pores, liver, kidneys and other channels of elimination are at work getting rid of some of these poisons and cell repair takes place, so that in seven, eight or nine hours the vibrations are restored to normal and the desire to waken and continue our activities becomes urgent.

So, the ancient yoga theory, though not couched in scientific parlance, is very similar to that propounded many thousands of years later. The yogis had no machines for measuring vibrations; nor for that matter can we measure the vibration of a single life cell. It is much too minute.

Poisons can be eliminated from the body in all sorts of ways; by cathartics, massage, exercise, deep breathing. Nevertheless, sleep is still needed to clean away certain toxins and residue which no other method can achieve. It does something which so far no scientist has been able either to measure or discover. Doctors can eliminate poisons by all sorts of artificial means, but sleep is still needed. For which I am truly grateful, for I enjoy my sleep.

In the chapter on Breathing I stated that the oxygen taken into the blood helps to burn the food we eat. Well, sleep is needed, perhaps, to get rid of some of the clinker still in the firebox.

During sleep the body is re-charged with vital energy, just as a battery is re-charged when it runs down, and the difference of cell vibration during walking and sleeping is analogous to the difference of potential between the battery terminals before and after re-charging.

There are more stupid adages coined about sleep and more nonsense written about it than almost any subject under the sun. Yogis say that the amount of absolute rest during any night of deep sleep is eleven and a half minutes, and I've seen it written by scientists that dreams take place in a fraction of a second. I cannot see how the figure eleven and a half minutes is reached, for the ancients had no watches and did not divide time into minutes. Even if they did, I am positive that the requirements of most people differ.

As we grow older, we need less sleep. We are less active, and eat less, and there is less poison to be eliminated from the body. Babies sleep from 15-18 hours out of every 24; a three-year-old child needs about 12 hours; a six-year-old 10 hours, and this need of 10 hours persists until adolescence is past. As soon as full growth is attained one needs an hour, and possibly two less of sleep. After the age of fifty, seven or even six hours should suffice, and very old people need extremely little sleep. They eat and exercise far less, and rest a good deal of the time.

Deep, sound sleep is necessary for health and that is just what some ten million people in Britain fail to get each night. Of these unfortunates there are two million who suffer from chronic insomnia. I term them unfortunates because though many of them are wealthy, they cannot buy that which almost any farm labourer can command. Or rather they will not buy it.

If most of the rich men who suffer from insomnia gave away their money, took jobs as navvies and farm labourers and broke stones on the road or tilled fields, they'd sleep soundly enough. But not one in a million will take this cheap and sensible cure. They can't. They're caught in traps as surely as any fox. They are so used to luxury that they cannot do without it. Their wives insist on mink coats. They must have a house in the country, a flat in town, two Rolls-Royces, a stomach ulcer and chronic indigestion. So they curse the government, rave about income tax, continue to cram themselves with rich food and milk of magnesia, and die without enjoying the real benefits that their money can buy.

I was reading some time ago how El Sayed Paschael Badraoui, the biggest landowner in Egypt, lies awake all night worrying about his money. He went to a specialist about his insomnia, and was told, "Throw you money away, and you will sleep soundly." But apparently he prefers to hang on to his wealth—and his insomnia.

One of the functions of sleep is to restore the oxygen balance of the blood. During waking hours you take in about 40 per cent. of oxygen and give off about 60 per cent.; during sleep this process is reversed. You take in 60 per cent. and give off 40 per cent. It is during sleep that by some means yet not explained you fill your body with energy.

There are all sorts of fallacies about sleep. Some people imagine that two hours sleep before midnight are equal to four after. This theory is complete rubbish. Sleep is the same whether you have it during the day or after the hours of darkness, and many who work at night and sleep during the day keep excellent health once they become innured to the strange routine.

Another fallacy is to imagine that if you continue junketing the whole of one night, you can make up for the amount you have squandered by sleeping twice as long the next night; but it takes more than two nights of sound sleep to compensate for a wasted night. A man of exceptionally strong constitution may have many sleepless nights without feeling the effects immediately, but if he continues overdrawing on the bank of sleep he will soon be a physical and nervous bankrupt.

I play cricket with a young chap who is wonderfully gifted by Nature. He is big, strong, and has never had a serious illness. During the summer just gone, he played cards all one Friday night and cricket the following day. Saturday night was again wasted at the card table, from which he rose, stepped into his car, drove to Bournemouth, played cricket all day, had a late evening and reached London at three. He was at the office at nine on Monday morning. He confessed that he often misses a night's sleep in this way. He is a headstrong fellow, and unless he alters his nocturnal habits he will be an old man by the time he is fifty, if not earlier. I've seen many strong men abuse their bodies by starving them of sleep—and then suddenly crack.

One of the reasons why manual workers—outdoor workers in particular—sleep so soundly is that their hard physical work compels them to breathe deeply. By doing so they alter vastly the rate of vibration of their bodies, and sleep comes as a natural result, in order that this shall be equalised. Fresh air itself is a great sleep producer.

Once a man has made himself a master of yoga breathing and can concentrate effectively, he can do without many hours of sleep and retain his health at the same time.

This is true only of the student who studies and practises yoga for fifteen or twenty years, devoting himself to exercises and breathing for hours each day. It cannot be achieved by the dabbler who practises asanas and breathing for fifteen or twenty minutes a day. Few masters of yoga sleep more than three or four hours of the twenty-four.

But fifteen or twenty minutes of yoga each day is enough to enable anyone to master the art of sound sleep at will.

Yogis are not the only people who have discovered that Man can do without a full eight hours each night without impairing his efficiency. Years ago I read of the experiments of Professor Stockman of Heidelberg, who persuaded a number of people, all doing different work, to go to bed at seven in the evening. He woke them at 11.30, after which they worked, read or amused themselves all night. In the morning they were all fresh and full of vitality and worked throughout the day without feeling sleepy. One of his guinea pigs, a professor aged sixty, walked 50 miles after waking—a feat at any age—and gave a lecture after his walk. At the end of it he said he was not more tired than if he had slept normally.

I was so impressed by this experiment that I tried it. I went to bed at seven one winter's evening and my alarm clock woke me precisely at 11.30. All night I read and worked, and the following morning was as fresh as if I had obtained my normal quota of sleep.

The main snag in this method is that one goes to bed at seven, when most normal people begin the evening, and when one wakes at eleven thirty it is too late for visiting, entertaining, or the theatre. Also, one has an eerie feeling being awake all night, alone. It seemed so unnatural that I did not continue the experiment.

The mind as well as the body is invigorated during sleep. The resting brain assimilates nourishment and energy. Research into the brain began some fifty years ago, and even to-day only certain areas of the brain have been fully explored. Professor Adrian, at Cambridge, Professor R. J. A. Berry, and scientists like Pitt, MacCulloch and Wiener in America have done a tremendous amount of work on the brain as well as the nervous system, and they liken that part of the brain which recognises words, colours and sounds to a huge calculating machine. The mechanics of hearing and seeing are being explored, but little is known about Sleep and the Unconscious Mind.

We do know, however, that the over-tired neurones or nerve cells—there are 9,200,000,000 neurones in the cerebral cortex—are fed with electrical impulses, just as a storage battery is charged, during sleep. Some day the exact source from which this energy is drawn, and the way in which the cells are replenished, will be known, but it is doubtful whether we shall ever be able to improve on Nature's method of resting the brain and body.

Professor Adrian says that electrical impulses radiate from the brain and when the potential (electrical pressure) between the sense organs and the cortex is equalised we fall asleep, for then there is no electrical activity in certain nerve centres. Narcotics taken by those who suffer from insomnia have the effect of adulterating the chemical sources of this electricity, and achieve the same result. But the cells are never properly re-charged by this method, which is the reason why those who resort to drugs awaken tired and unrefreshed.

A rested brain is able to tackle problems that baffled one the night before, and it is excellent advice to sleep on any problem that eludes solution at night. Mathematical geniuses like Henri Poincare, nephew of the French President, Boule, William Rowan Hamilton, Descartes and others all experienced brilliant flashes of inspiration which solved intricate problems—after a night of sound sleep.

For some lucky people, among whom I count myself, night is a period of rest, relaxation and invigoration. I welcome sleep. I look forward to the hour when I can lay my head on the pillow, relax my limbs and shut out the problems of this world. Unconsciously we draw upon the forces of Nature.

For others, sleep is a period of torture and restlessness; of tossing and turning; of mulling over troubles and problems that should be left behind. The sleepless find that the brain works at racing speed, till when morning breaks, it is desperately tired. For a third type, night is a well of terror. The imagination runs riot and all sorts of horrible visions and nightmares make darkness unbearable.

The way to command sleep is first to obtain perfect health. When this is done you can forget the body, control your mind and relax utterly. Sleep will follow instantly. This can be achieved by practising the asanas and yoga breathing. So conquer the flesh that you can ignore it. These—and the art of lying in the correct position in bed. And if you are not in good health, a modified diet. Sometimes before retiring I have taken, for my supper, two cups of strong coffee and a whole cucumber, and nothing else; simply because I fancied this somewhat odd combination, and I have slept as soundly as if I had been knocked on the head. I remember once sleeping through a minor earthquake after just such a supper, waking only when I was hurled on to the floor by the rocking of the bed.

There are two excellent positions for relaxing and obtaining complete rest. One is known as *Savasana* (corpse pose) or *mrtasana* (dead pose). Lie on your back on a firm, flat bed, without a pillow. Close your eyes and relax your limbs utterly. This is not easy. Take each part of your body in turn; eyes, mouth, chin, tongue, neck, arms, hands, stomach, thighs, legs, feet, toes. Then start again and go through the entire list. Imagine that you are sinking right through the bed. You may have to relax each organ or limb a number of times before complete relaxation is achieved, though the possibility is that you will fall asleep without quite knowing when or how.

The best pose for restful sleep, however, is the yoga pose known as *dradhasana*, or the firm pose, and though it may seem uncomfortable or unnatural at first, it is really the most comfortable position in which to sleep.

Use a soft, low pillow and place the head firmly on it, giving the neck no strain and no work to do. Sleep on the right side with the legs straight down the bed, but not stiff. Place the left leg over and along it, with the left foot either slightly overlapping the right, or behind it. The left arm, with the palm facing down, lies along the body and thigh; the right arm slightly in front of the body. If no pillow is used, the right arm may be folded and the right arm—wrist and hand—placed under the head.

Once mastered, this position brings sound, restful sleep. There is no undue weight on the heart, and it is the best possible position for the stomach to empty itself. *Dradhasana* is not the result of a sudden brainwave on the part of a crank, but the outcome of years of experiment. I find it an exceedingly comfortable and restful position.

113

If you've tried all other methods of inducing sleep and have failed to get it, try Yoga breathing and asanas. Practise yoga methods of concentration and relaxation, observe their rules of hygiene and diet, and sleep in the position the yogis advocate.

Sleep, once the most natural thing in the world, seems unnatural to millions of tortured people to-day. It cannot be bought, and insomnia is part of the heavy price we pay for civilisation. We can fly, but we can't sleep!

CHAPTER VIII

Yoga and the Emotions

WITHIN the mind of every sane and many insane persons there are powerful forces at work; forces which can heal and bring happiness, or disrupt and destroy. We call these forces *emotions*, and they are, more often than not, the outcome of a self-generated power known as *imagination*.

In India the *kaviraj* (herbalist) or *hakim* (doctor) on being introduced into the sick room does not exhort his patient to say " ninety-nine " or request him to put out his tongue. He inquires instead, " Apke mizaj kaesi hai ? " which being translated, means, " How is your mind ? " (mood or temper).

In the opinion of the yogis, imagination, the generating force behind emotion, is the most powerful in the world. Bullets and bombs wreck the lives of millions; imagination, and the emotions its creates, destroys thousands of millions.

Only within recent years—since the advent of men like Freud, Jung, Adler and Havelock Ellis—have we begun to realize how tremendous are these forces for good or for evil; for sickness and for health. Because of their ideas and teachings a new race of men have come into being, known as psychologists, who study the victims of emotion. They try to get their patients to sublimate or neutralize, so that their emotions do not wreck their lives.

There is nothing new on earth. The wheel has turned its full circle, and psychologists and psychiatrists are trying to do now, what yogis did many centuries ago. They are delving into the mind, learning about the processes of thought, and trying to undo the harm caused by certain emotions.

Centuries ago, when men knew less about such matters, the victims of certain chronic emotions and persistent ideas were said to harbour evil spirits and demons, and men who exhibited such peculiarities were stoned or burnt at the stake. The fathers of the Roman Catholic Church advised either sublimation or suppression. They did not realize that suppressing an emotion is like pressing down a powerful coiled spring, or sitting on a boiling kettle, every vent of which has been soldered.

As far as I can discover, the only ancient people who made a scientific study of emotion, were the yogis of India, and the Chinese. According to Father Amiot's famous work on China, there was a system of movements and postures to preserve health and cure disease. The pose adopted in some of the postures was similar to the Lotus Seat of yoga. Amiot writes: " Yu Kang Chi, the second Emperor *before* Foo Hi. (Foo Hi was emperor in 3,468 B.C.). During his reign it was nearly always raining, and unhealthy diseases inundated the earth, so to speak. The Emperor made his subjects perform certain military exercises every day. The movements they were obliged to perform contributed not less to the cure of those who were weak than to the preservation in health of those who were well."

Of the Chinese methods we know little, for their records have been lost. But yoga is still preserved.

Emotion is a combination of many factors. Often it is an automatic reaction to an emergency. In cases of intense fear or immense happiness, the body acts instantly because of almost instantaneous reflexes. You hear a funny story or a joke, or see a fat man slide on a banana skin, and you react without conscious thought. You hear a loud crash and instantly the defensive mechanism that has been developed in the course of millions of years of Man's survival, comes into action. You crouch, or throw yourself flat, or lift an arm to ward off a blow. You experience fear; possibly a sense of faintness. Sometimes the colour drains from your face and sweat bursts upon your brow.

The shock that follows sudden, violent emotion can kill a man instantly, or derange his mind.

Once I was present when a cat was brought into a laboratory and placed under an X-ray. A vicious dog was then introduced into the room, and instantly made for the cat, which stood on a high table. Out came its claws; it arched its back and spat at the dog. One could see a sudden, involuntary contraction of the cat's stomach.

Experiments on human beings have shown that when suffering from fear and anxiety, the stomach contracts, the digestive juices dry up, and a meal eaten under such circumstances cannot be properly assimilated into the system. So, if a person is suffering stress or strain, fear, anxiety or any violent emotion whatsoever, don't urge him to eat.

A person who has suffered a bereavement, for instance, does not want to eat, but solicitous relatives force food upon him ' to keep up his strength.' Food eaten under such conditions not only does no good, but can cause digestive trouble.

A physician named Hornborg had in his charge a boy suffering from gastric fistula. There was an abnormal opening in his stomach. Hornborg took advantage of this opening to study the flow of gastric juices. When appetizing food was offered the boy, he watered at the mouth and digestive juices were secreted in the stomach and the intestine. On one occasion the food was taken away; the boy began to cry and the flow of juices ceased. The food was then offered again, but though his tears had stopped and the boy was apparently normal, *the juices refused to flow*.

Beating, scolding or threatening children at meal times, so that they weep and are upset, is just about the worst treatment any parent can give a child.

In the thirteenth century the Emperor Frederick II, who knew nothing about the results of emotional stress, decided upon an interesting experiment. He wished to discover which language, if any, a child would speak if it were entirely untaught; whether it would babble in its mother tongue, or speak French, German, or one of the ancient languages like Latin, Greek, or Hebrew.

He issued orders that a number of homeless babes were to be housed under one roof and given every care and attention by skilled nurses; but the nurses were ordered— under penalty of death—neither to speak to the infants nor show them affection.

Though infants cannot speak or understand the spoken word they respond to the innumerable signs of affection made by mothers and nurses; crooning noises, rocking, chucking under the chin, tickles, hugs and kisses, baby talk, facial expressions, and gestures of love. And because none of these signs of affection were forthcoming, *every infant wilted* and died!

I have had yogis tell me that emotions and thoughts are solid things, like tables and chairs, and in the light of the very latest findings of our scientists, there is comparatively little difference. Jeans and Eddington and Millikan tell us that the atom is so tiny that five million atoms can be placed side by side on the diameter of a single pencil dot, and that each atom is a universe in itself, and is composed of protons, electrons, neutrons, positrons and alpha particles. In a single germ cell there are something like eight million billions of atoms; and in a drop of water, several thousand million billions ! No mind can conceive such minutiæ, so it is possible that thought may be composed of particles which we can neither see, hear nor feel.

When you are charged with emotion, the chemistry of the blood changes; pleasant emotions charge the blood with life-giving and strengthening chemicals; whereas unpleasant emotions poison the blood.

If one can hate long and fiercely enough, malignant growths resulting in cancer, may result. Watch young people in love. They go off their food because they are labouring under excitement and the stress of pleasant emotion. They keep fit and well, despite the lack of nourishment, because pleasant emotions, the product of their imagination, enrich the blood with vital chemicals. On the other hand, let one lover suspect the other of playing false, and emotions such as anxiety and jealousy will wreck his health.

All you've got to do is to observe and check your results. And that is what the yogis must have done over a period of centuries before they synthesized their ideas.

Most forms of emotion need some physical outlet. When overcome by fear or panic a man can run faster than his normal pace, or fight with twice his normal strength if cornered. This is because the adrenal gland pours a small quantity of adrenalin into the blood, which makes the heart beat faster, increases the circulation, makes the hair rise, the pupils dilate, and enlarges the lung passages to take in more air. The extra physical exertion enables the blood to utilize the adrenalin. But if there is no physical exertion after a violent upsurge of emotion, then a feeling of weakness and limpness sets in, and if the various substances injected into the blood while under the stress of emotion are not dissipated by physical action, their accumulation is likely to cause organic disease.

Sometimes, during emergency glucose is thrown into the bloodstream to give instant energy to the muscles, and if the need is urgent the amount injected into the blood can be so large that some of it overflows into the urine. Athletes sometimes try to provide extra energy for a race by eating a tablespoon of molasses, black treacle or brown sugar an hour or two before the event.

I have at times taken note of my own reactions under the stimulus of fear or other emotion. I remember being caught one night in the streets of London during a particularly bad raid in 1940. I had no tin hat, which during a raid always gave me a feeling of extraordinary security. As bomb fragments were falling like rain, I took shelter in a doorway. As the barrage grew heavier and nearer I took note of my thoughts and reactions.

My mind was calm and clear, and I felt that it would be a pity to be blotted out just when I was capable of enjoying life to the utmost. My mind was unafraid, but my body produced all the symptoms of fear; my heart beat faster, the skin on the backs of my hands was cold, my breathing was rapid, and I felt a slight contraction of my stomach. My limbs were slowly growing more rigid, as if expecting a blow at any moment. So I decided to emerge and walk down the street with my mind on other things, and such is the power of the mind that my body was soon walking down Kensington High Street, while my mind was in the Thames Valley.

If you are afraid and let your imagination dwell on the unpleasant causes of your fear, panic is likely to set in, and you might lose control of your actions. The ability to concentrate and turn your thoughts in the direction you wish, are among the many things that yoga teaches. Another is the ability to make your mind a blank.

Many emotions—fear, anxiety, jealousy, envy—are induced and excited by the imagination. The man who will walk on a scaffolding three feet above the ground without the slightest trace of fear will tremble and shiver with fright if placed on the same scaffolding a hundred feet above the earth. I knew a man who in the dark walked calmly up a narrow path leading to the top of a mountain; but he was sick with fear next morning when asked to return the same way.

Thoughts, the winged messengers which cause emotion, leave their imprint not only on human character, but often on the face of a person. You can't, for twenty years wear an expression of envy, hatred or scorn, and then suddenly wipe it off as you would a layer of shaving cream. You can't laugh your way through life without wearing a mask of joy.

Imagination is a wonderful stimulus if controlled and used properly. All of us are Walter Mittys in some degree; if not, life would be unbearable for many.

Uncontrolled imagination makes us insane; perhaps not insane enough to be dumped into an asylum where at least we would be safe, but just insane enough to make ourselves and those around us miserable. A famous British doctor, William Tegner, says: " You can think yourself into having rheumatism or arthritis," and adds that one person out of every eight who consulted him was a " mind case."

As stated earlier, when physical effort is suddenly needed, the mind or *citta*, as the yogis term it, conjures up a crisis; automatically the glands pour secretions into the blood and this extra energy is used to contend with the crisis.

Much the same thing happens in the jungle of industry and commerce. Men are constantly faced by crises, and a series of sudden efforts is needed. The bloodstream is fortified by glandular secretions which are *not* used up in physical effort, and the result is that these secretions interfere with the digestive processes. Dr. Walter C. Alvarez, of the famous Mayo Clinic, Rochester, Minnesota, has written an excellent book on the subject, called, " Nervous Indigestion," which should be in the hands of all who are interested in the mind and its effect upon disease.

Any cult that relies on fear for results, or tries to repress its disciples, is fundamentally wrong. That is why yoga is a philosophy of happiness, contentment of mind and abounding health. It abolishes fear.

Misused, imagination can be disastrous. In the nineteen thirties Dr. Flanders Dunbar of New York, and colleagues, began an investigation into the various diseases that caused emotional upsets. They found that in some fifty per cent. of cases where heart trouble and diabetes were present, emotional factors made the illness much worse. When emotion is pent up and cannot be discharged in a natural way—usually by some physical activity—it discharges itself in the form of a disease. If a person suffers from some organic disease, but is made happy and contented, his cure is always much accelerated.

Dr. Edwin Moos reported the case of a man suffering with systolic blood pressure of 280, who in addition had a lung disorder. Tests showed traces of albumen in his urine, and though he was rested and given the appropriate drugs, there was little change in his condition. Accidently he discovered that the man had wronged his wife and that they had separated. He arranged for a meeting at which the pair discussed their troubles and a reconcilliation was effected. Almost at once the patient's blood pressure fell to 150, and later to 130; his lung healed and the albumen in his urine disappeared.

Doctors and scientists all over the world are now conducting experiments to find out the connection between emotions and disease. Dr. Stanley Cobb, of the Massachusetts General Hospital, Boston, made a study of patients with a variety of complaints—asthma, arthritis, colitis, migrane. He had a number of personal interviews with those suffering from mucous colitis, and found that 96 per cent. of them had, bottled up inside them, feelings of resentment against some person or persons; 75 per cent. were depressed in spirit; 68 per cent were afflicted by feelings of guilt. All these grudges boiled up inside them and either caused or aggravated their disease.

Shell shock is the result of a violent form of emotion, and men suffering with shell shock have had their blood so poisoned that their minds are deranged.

The yogi disciple who has not yet mastered his emotions is advised never to eat while frightened, worried or in a station of tension. Among the earliest tribes in India there originated an ordeal that has come down to the twentieth century, known as ' trial by rice eating.' A priest consecrates rice, and each suspect is given a handful to chew. He tells them that the rice of the guilty man will remain dry, and at the end of the ordeal that chewed by the guilty man *is* almost invariably dry ! In his mind he believes that he will be found out, and fear dries up the normal saliva secretion, or vastly reduces it, so that the rice he takes out of his mouth looks very different from the pulpy messes that the others spit forth.

The ' truth machine ' is based on the same principle. The electro-encephalograph records two types of waves, alpha and beta, which are formed by the activity of the brain. Fear and emotional upsets cause a damping down of the alpha waves, which normally predominate. When a victim is tested and beta waves alone are picked up and recorded, those working the machine are almost certain that the man is guilty.

Every emotion that you experience, helps to mould your character. Every emotion that you wilfully indulge in makes you what you are; physically and mentally. That is why you should be able to control, not repress or sublimate your emotions. Every time a highly strung athlete enters a boxing ring, walks out to bat in a cricket match, or lines up for the start of a race, emotional stresses are caused, and researchers have discovered that emotion at the start of a race, for instance, can be so intense that when samples of runners' urine were analysed they contained such a high percentage of sugar that they were said to have ' temporary diabetes.'

Yoga lays down eight stages of discipline: *yamas* and *niyamas*, which are the negative and positive ethical codes; *asanas*—postures or exercises; *pranayama*, or yogic breathing; *pratyahara*—withdrawal or control of the senses; *dharana*, meditation; *dhyana*, contemplation; and *samadhi*, isolation.

To practise each stage independently of the others nullifies its value and defeats its object, though for conquest of the emotions, *pranayama* and *pratyahara* are the key stages.

The mastery of logic and the art of discussion are all part of yoga, for only by fathoming the nature of existence can one come by truth. At every step one must ask, " How ? " " Where ? " " When ? " and " Why ? " Nothing should be taken for granted.

The yogi examines himself in relation to the rest of the universe, and learns to take an objective view of all events. It is because of the purely personal view we take of events, persons and objects, that emotions have their effect upon us. He neither suppresses nor ignores external things. He merely regards them objectively. When a yogi has schooled himself thoroughly he reaches that state when his emotions are neither *in* nor *of* him. He refuses to let his *emotions* develop into *passions*. *Emotion* is an agitation of the feelings produced by *imagination*; *passion* is a form of suffering, and is the result of acute emotion usually over a long period. Violent passions can make a person very ill indeed, or warp his outlook and judgment.

As most of us grow older, our passions and emotions are less violent, for age has a mellowing effect. The impact of events does not leave so deep a mark, and one is not as harrowed by the same things as one would be in youth. Yoga teaches that death and what we term disaster, are not so dire as they seem; that loss of life is merely a phase in eternal existence. Yogis were the first not only to abolish the fear that human beings have of death, but to prepare for and welcome it when it comes. Death is like taking off one suit of clothes—the body—and putting on fresh raiment.

They consider sublimation to be merely substitution; an evasion. Yoga is a philosophy of experience. The Guru (master) does not say to his Chela (disciple): " Refrain from this or that experience because it is bad. Don't drink alcoholic beverages because you may become a drunkard." A man must try everything himself, in order to discover truly whether it is good or bad. And only after reflection, discussion and meditation can he decide. The yoga attitude is non-normal. To him nothing is either good or bad except in relation to something else.

Our civilization is so hedged in and bounded by rules which have come into being for the convenience of the majority, that we develop complexes about things that are perfectly natural. We even regard sex as something not quite nice and unless one discusses it in the high-faluting language of the pseudo-intellectual, it is not considered a fit subject in the company of women, who incidentally play, I believe, a fairly important part in sex relations.

One of the results is that every night a bunch of bald-headed salacious old men with opera glasses glued to their eyes occupy the first two rows of a certain well known theatre scarcely a hammer's throw from Piccadilly Circus, and feast their eyes on models undressing in public. Such men are the products of sexual repression.

Repressions of any sort sooner or later result in what are generally known as " nerves." A London specialist said not long ago that " a jolly good row now and again clears the air and is good for nerves." But the follower of yoga has no need to quarrel violently. He learns to control the imaginings and emotions that result in " jolly good rows."

According to Sir Farquhar Buzzard, Physician in Ordinary to the King, we lose something like 30,000,000 working weeks each year because of people who are ill from nervous disorders.

" It was found recently," he said, " that one in fourteen of the working population suffers from nervous disorders to the extent of needing treatment. Of the people examined, 20 per cent. had less severe symptoms, and another 20 per cent. showed odd symptoms. At least one third of the sickness in this country is due to causes which are not organic in origin."

Who can compute the harm and illness wrought by the present housing shortage ? Millions have to live with people with whom they cannot exist in harmony.

Who can estimate the harm done by our present social and economic system which prevents most men marrying till after thirty ? Millions of girls remained unmarried, and the cumulative repressions, if turned into motive power, would be sufficient to propel the entire air forces of all the nations to Mars and back.

How many realize the harm done by the present marriage system, where a man with more than one wife is a criminal ? For most men are polygamous by nature.

It is possible, however, even in this unnatural environment, to live a useful, contented life, by controlling the forces which make most of us want to " run off the rails " at some time or another.

CHAPTER IX

Vibrations and Colour

MANY of the results achieved by the yogis are obtained through the medium of vibration and colour. They laid down the theory that in the body there are 14 main *nadis* or nerves and 350,000 branches, each finer than the finest hair, having their centre in the pelvic area known as *muladhara*. The *nadis* radiate to every part of the body and sensations are carried along them.

By the exercise of the imagination, or the action of external factors, messages, like currents of electricity, flow along these *nadis*, carrying sensations which result in emotions, and, as pointed out in the previous chapter, cause chemical changes in the blood and physical changes in the organs, which bring about either health or sickness.

I do not know how the number 350,000 was arrived at, but I suspect that it was an arbitrary figure, for there is no vestige of evidence to suggest that the early yogis conducted clinical or laboratory experiments, such as carried out by present day researchers. Whether this figure is accurate, matters little. What matters is that they hit upon a fundamental truth which accords with modern findings. We know that the nerves are mediums of sensation, and that without them we could neither think nor feel, for it is along them than instantaneous messages pass from the various parts of the body to the brain, and from the brain to various parts of the body.

The yogis believe that in every human being there lies dormant a kind of psychic energy known as *kundalini*, and that by means of certain yogic practices this can be released through the *shushumna* or spinal cord so that it makes its way to the *sahasrara*—upper cerebrum. When this happens the subject gains power over his thoughts and emotions; he can regulate them and is their master, not their slave.

Kundalini may be released by the regular practise of yoga breathing exercises, asanas, exercises in meditation and concentration, and by the repetition of mantras and sounds which arouse vibrations throughout the body. In the picturesque, symbolic phraseology of yoga, *kundalini* is known as ' serpent power ' and lies coiled at the root of the spinal cord, or *brahmadanda*.

To the man of poetic feeling the symbolic language in which all Hindu writing is couched, is delightful; to the scientist or the purely practical person it is usually irritating, for all meaning seems wrapped in a cocoon of verbiage. It must never be forgotten that yoga teachings were handed down by word of mouth to a population that was largely illiterate and highly superstitious. The wonder of it is that so much that is comprehensible remains.

It does not matter whether scientists admit the existence of *kundalini* or not. The true scientist will reserve his opinion, for he is the last person to claim that scientific knowledge is complete. It is sufficient to say that men— not only yogis—have performed amazing feats after controlling and harnessing *kundalini*. But long before a student releases *kundalini* he must become an adept at exercises such as the *bandhas*, *naulis* and *mudras*, which exercise his abdomen and spine and add vastly to his store of nervous energy. I have practised *bandhas* and *naulis* for some thirty years, and one of many benefits is the complete banishment of constipation. A further stage is *basti* in which, by means of breath control and a contraction of the abdominal group of muscles, a vacuum is formed and water drawn into the colon. All these are merely stages on the road which leads to the eventual release of *kundalini*, and it is well worth going to a great deal of trouble to master them, for they give the body abounding energy and a feeling of tremendous lightness.

In order to achieve such results the student must be careful to practise all the branches laid down, and not merely one or two to the exclusion of the others.

Among the many exercises are those based on the theory that vibrations help to give one control over the body, and if the right vibrations are used, the body can become vigorous and healthy, and the senses more acute; if the wrong vibrations are practised, ill health or even death may ensue. One of the most common yogic practices is to utter the syllable OM in a resonant manner, by letting the sound start in the throat and end on the lips. Repeat this sonorously till it resounds in your head like a bell.

The repetition of this syllable in such a way is an excellent device for bringing back to its focal point a wandering mind. It is advisable, of course, not to repeat OM in the way suggested, in the foyer of a hotel or a crowded railway carriage or people will think—and justifiably so—that you are mad. It is, however, a wonderful exercise for focusing the mind, for while repeating the syllable OM, force your mind to conjure up a vision of the letters, about a foot high, in green, this being a soothing colour.

The yogis have devised numerous *mantras* or incantations, which, when repeated again and again cause vibrations to flow along the *nadis* and produce healing or beneficial effects on the body and mind.

All this may seem sheer idiocy to the reader who has no first hand experience of yoga; but it isn't. Within the last thirty years scientists in Europe and America have discovered that vibrations are a form of energy, and that every object we see, hear or feel is composed of vibrations and nothing else. Objects are different in texture and hardness, and liquids vary in viscosity because the energy which goes to make them up vibrates at a different rate. We know, too, that noise—this includes all sounds, pleasant as well as unpleasant—tends either to heal or destroy, and vibrations, when controlled by Man, can be made to do all sorts of wonderful things.

Scientists now understand the apparent unreasoning antipathy to noise shown by men like Schopenhauer, Goethe, Kant, Mozart and Lichtenberg. They were sensitive men living among the noisiest and most boisterous people in Europe. Schopenhauer could not tolerate hammering, the barking of dogs, crying children or the cracking of whips; Mozart howled in agony when a bugle was blown in his presence.

Yet, in our modern existence we are compelled to suffer hooters, sirens, whistles, rivotting machines, pneumatic drills, the frenzied yelling of football crowds, travelling loudspeakers and the constant drone of planes and other noises which help to make life frightful.

The yogis warned their disciples to flee periodically from too much noise, to seek the solitude of the Himalayas, for they realized what havoc can be wrought by noise.

According to Dr. Foster Kennedy, an American authority, loud noises tend to decrease the gastric juices of the stomach and cause nervous indigestion. The bursting of a paper bag behind a victim's back, which practical jokers consider immense fun, raises the blood pressure of the brain to a greater degree than it is raised either by morphine or nitro-glycerine, two of the most powerful drugs for increasing brain pressure.

Discordant noises often produce nervous indigestion in sensitive, highly strung people. In fact, the unseen and unheard vibrations in a discordant family atmosphere can make a sensitive person seriously ill.

Dr. Freeman, an eminent brain specialist, says that excessive noise causes changes in the brain, which is composed of proteins, and that insanity can be produced by noise alone. He cites the case of a woman so crippled by rheumatism that she could only wheel herself about in an armchair. Next to her room lived a man with a powerful radio, which, despite her entreaties, he refused to tone down. One morning she was driven to such a frenzy of desperation that she wheeled herself to a window, crawled painfully over the sill and dropped a hundred feet into merciful oblivion.

The example of the effects of bell ringing given in *The Nine Tailors* by Dorothy L. Sayers, could well have been taken from life, for there are cases where men have been locked inadvertently in belfries and killed by the continuous clanging of the bells.

Dr. Charles Warren, a famous ear specialist, says that when thrown into a noisy atmosphere, Nature, as a protective measure, thickens the ear drums, till ultimately one becomes deaf; then, one avenue through which sensations reach us, is closed and our sensitivity lessened. This, for a student of yoga, who desires above all things, to increase his sense of perception, is disastrous.

" One day," prophesied Edison, " men of the future will live and work in a vacuum of silence." He visualized cities of the future where noise will be so great that in order to save us all from madness, Nature will turn us deaf.

The yogis know a good deal about the healing as well as the destructive vibrations, and some of this knowledge is incorporated into Indian music, which to most British ears is devoid either of tone, timbre or harmony. To Indians, the skill of the player, the correctness with which he handles his instrument or voice, and the rhythm of his song are all important. To a European, an Indian voice when raised in song seems shrill, harsh and nasal because the notes are sustained without breathing, and are produced from the back of the nose.

The monotony of Indian music and singing is painful to most European ears that are not trained to detect the microtones in Indian music. All ancient Hindu music is allied either to religion or the occult. The gods were supposed to have invented their musical instruments; their notes have gender. The male note is the *rag* or *raga* (this has no connection whatsoever, with rag or ragtime) and the female notes are *raginas*. They believe in the power of vibrations—Indian music is essentially vibratory—to destroy solid objects, either by shattering them or by setting them on fire, and to heal sick minds and bodies. In India there is a melody known as the *Dipak Raga*, which if played correctly is supposed to produce intense heat, and then fire.

An old legend says that Akbar the Great (1556-1605) once commanded a yogi, a wonderful musician, to sing the *Dipak Raga*. The mystic, despite offers of wealth, postponed the exhibition of his skill because he realized that he could not sing the *Dipak Raga* without awakening supernatural powers. Came a day, however, when his excuses ran dry, so he decided, as a safety measure, to sing while standing in the River Jumna up to his neck in water.

As the notes emerged, the water grew warmer, till eventually it boiled; but as Akbar refused to give the singer permission to stop, he eventually burst into flames and was burnt to cinder !

The story is doubtless apocryphal, but there are so many legends about similar miracles wrought by singers and musicians that there can be little doubt that the ancient Hindus knew something about the extraordinary power of vibrations.

They had no instruments to measure sound in decibels or to record the exact frequency of waves; they did not realize that the limit of ultrasonics is 16,000,000 sound waves a second; that the audible range is from 16 to 20,000; that the characteristic pitch of a man's voice is 250 and a woman's 125; or that waves between zero frequency and 16 come within the scale of infrasonics.

They knew none of these things. That is why their discoveries in that distant age were as astounding. Today, by means of ultrasonics it is possible to make chips of wood burst into flames from a distance, cook a dinner, shatter a glass dish or kill bacteria. Science has proved that the destruction of the walls of Jericho by the blowing of trumpets was not impossible, for a scientist in America has made a machine which produces the noise and vibrations of 33,000 trumpets sounded simultaneously, and by this means has knocked down walls; Another American, Charles Kellog, can put out a candle flame some twenty feet away from him by whistling ultra high notes, and he has a device fitted to his car which starts the engine when he whistles.

Since the beginning of this century doctors, musicians and scientists have collaborated in musical experiments to heal the sick. They have cured epileptics and restored sanity to the mad; they have raised the spirits of the depressed and improved their health; they have induced sleep in the minds of patients with insomnia and have abolished many nervous and stomach complaints. Now we are learning the reasons; once we did not know. When Saul was stricken with melancholia, David the son of Jesse was summoned, and we are told that " David took an harp and played with his hand; so Saul was refreshed and well, and the evil spirit departed from him."

So when yoga lays it down that certain sounds have to be uttered in a specific way or reiterated monotonously, we can only deduce that men in the distant past tried out the formula and achieved the desired result. Not only that; the formula must have been successful time and again, otherwise it would never have been incorporated into their philosophy. It is regrettable that for the benefit of posterity, if nor no other reason, the details of their researches and experiments were not preserved.

Few people think about the effects of sound, but when they are told about them, they agree readily that sounds affect them deeply. Who, at a rugby match between Wales and one of the other countries can remain unmoved

when 20,000 magnificent voices are raised in singing
" Cwm Rhondda ? " The Welsh must have won many
a game with the sheer physical and mental reaction
caused by the singing of such songs as " Sospon Fach,"
" Ton y Botel," and " Dai bach y sojer."

Sounds, sometimes in the form of inspiring music, can
rouse lethargic people to great heights. When Europe
was smitten by the Great Plague in 1679, a huge pit was
dug in Vienna and thousands of bodies of the dead and
half-dead were dumped there. Among them was an
itinerant street singer named Augustin. He was not dead,
but merely drunk. At dawn he emerged and besottedly
began to troll " Ach ! Du Lieber Augustin." The
refrain was so infectious that a great crowd collected,
the pall of gloom was lifted, men began to dance and
be of good cheer; and this feeling spread so rapidly that
soon Germany and all Europe was revived by the magic
of a single tune.

Music not only revives; it inflames. We know that
Claude Rouget de Lisle's " Marseillaise," swept France
into a frenzy of patriotic fervour, and the music of
Edouard Remenyi so inflamed the Austro-Hungarians
that the authorities forbade him from playing his violin
and he was six times sentenced to death ' *in absentia* '
by various courts for defying them.

The right sort of music can achieve almost any effect.
It can turn people slothful and hypnotise them. In the
18th century Domenico Cimarosa, composer of 47
successful grand operas was exiled for life from Italy
because King Ferdinand feared that his music would
cause Neapolitans to lose their fighting ability ! And we
know only too well what happened in 1940 when 250,000

citizens of Oslo were mesmerized by the rollicking music of German bands.

The bands played continuously in the park alongside the Carl Johan Boulevard for two days, and the people flocked to hear them. While thus distracted, German ' tourists,' armed to the teeth, landed in the city in small groups till there were 20,000 of them. Then they battered Oslo into submission.

Sound has almost illimitable power either to cure or kill. In Italy in the 17th century there broke out a terrible plague known as St. Vitus' Dance, or as we know it today, chorea. A great physician of the period, Baglivi, resorted to music when all else had failed. He formed ' medical orchestras,' that played gay, lively tunes; particularly one type of music. And because it was thought that St. Vitus' Dance was caused by the sting of the huge tarentula spider, the music which cured it was named the Tarentella, and is today one of Italy's most popular dances.

Modern physicians have barely touched the fringe of this tremendous new science, and when ultimately there begins a serious collaboration between doctors and musicians, thousands without hope will be restored to health.

The University of Banaras has invited a group of musicians from various parts of the world to start research in musical therapy under the direction of the Indian vocalist, Pandit Omkarnath Thakore. His chief assistant will be the Italian, Alain Danjelou, who has been studying musical therapy for years. Both Thakore and Danjelou believe that a combination of melodious and harmonious sounds can do much to restore the sick to health.

In our groping fashion we feel that certain sounds are beneficial. They soothe and calm one, and assist the mind to relax. The Roman Catholic Church makes excellent us of this idea in its litanies and responses, most of which are quite meaningless when repeated parrot fashion —as they usually are. It is this, as well as their wonderful singing that makes the devout feel ' good ' when they emerge from the reverent gloom of a church into the harsh sunlight, for the early Christians knew the value of music, colour, glorious architecture and ritual.

The yogis do the same thing. Their cathedrals are the lofty Himalayas, more inspiring than any edifice that Man can erect. Their colours are the tints and hues of Nature, which put the cleverest artists to shame. They make use of the sonorous, rotund phrases of the *mantras*, which set up the necessary vibrations in the body and bring *samadhi* one step nearer.

The English, if hardly as musical as the Italians or the Germans, have an unrivalled heritage of beautiful poetry. Some time ago letters were printed in a Sunday paper, in which readers asked why they were moved on reading aloud certain passages of poetry. One woman stated that the reading aloud of Milton's *Lycidias* always upset her, and when she came to the lines " Begin then, Sisters of the Sacred Well . . . " tears invariably flowed. The same thing happened when she read *The Phoenix and the Turtle*, the whole of Coleridge's *Kubla Khan*, and parts of *Childe Harold's Pilgrimage*, by Byron, particularly the passage which goes " O Albuera, glorious field of grief."

This writer confessed that she was filled with what she termed ' ecstatic woe.'

Others wrote in, agreeing with her. Some stated that to them poetry was more physical than intellectual, and one man testified that if he thought of certain lines of poetry while shaving, his skin bristled so that his razor ceased to act. Shivers ran down his spine, his throat contracted, and tears came into his eyes.

We don't know why certain sounds have certain effects on people; or why some sounds effect certain people in one way and others in an entirely different way. To a friend of mine who is tone deaf, the clanking of a tram and a nocturne by Chopin sound alike. Baudelaire once said: " I love Wagner, but the music I prefer is that of a cat hung up by its tail outside a window, trying to stick to the panes of glass with its claws. There is an odd grating on the glass which I find at the same time strange, irritating and singularly harmonious."

Strange that we, in this scientific age should be experimenting with a problem that the yogis grappled with centuries ago. Truly, there is nothing new under the sun.

The yogis also say that there is an affinity between sound and colour; that each note of music has a corresponding hue. They didn't put it quite that way; they say that each colour has a corresponding number of sound vibrations.

It is a peculiar fact that most people are almost completely insensitive to variations in colour. The conditions of so-called civilized existence have rendered millions mentally colour blind. They seldom consciously see colours in front of them, and if they do, the gradations in colour and shade do not impinge themselves on their consciousness. Once I asked a group of students to whom I was lecturing, what the colour was of a certain wall we passed daily. They were all adults and keenly appreciative of the good things of life. Some said " Red," and others " Grey," so we went out and examined the wall which seemed to shimmer with reflected colour in the sunlight. We counted no fewer than thirty distinct colours in the brickwork, and had we taken more trouble, could possibly have doubled that number. Some of them were, for the first time, seeing that wall as an artist would have seen it.

Some people are highly colour conscious; others not at all. Those who are—artists, dress designers, house furnishers, window dressers, etc.—arrange and colour their surroundings to suit their tastes and moods, and are all the happier and healthier for the trouble they take. Insensitive people do nothing about it, but without realizing it, colours seep into minds and bodies, affecting both, for colours not only reflect and absorb heat, but for all we know, have other properties yet undiscovered.

Colour is, of course, an optical illusion and depends upon many factors, among which are: daylight, gaslight, electric light, the quantity, quality and concentration of light; the angle at which light bears on the object; refraction; one's eyesight, and the condition of one's stomach, mind and mood.

People do not realize that neither the rainbow nor the feathers on a peacock's tail are coloured. Each is an optical illusion; the rainbow by refraction; the colour of the feathers is caused by the flues of the feathers bending the light. Boil the tail of a peacock or subject it to chemical analysis, and you won't extract a drop of colour from it. There isn't any there.

Yet, each of these illusions has some effect upon the human mind, stirs up some emotion, and helps to make us either better or worse in health.

In front of me as I sit and write, is a picture, *Red Horses* by Franz Marc. It is a delightful colour sketch, no worse for the fact that the horses are red. He may actually have seen them as red, for the warmth and vitality thrown off by red is in his work.

That the yogis bothered at all about colour is amazing, for savage races see and record four colours, at most. Even the ancient Greeks, whose culture we still consider unequalled in Europe, named but two colours; to them both the sky and sea were black !

The yogis term yellow the colour of the mind; thus their *swamis* clothe themselves in saffron robes. Red is the colour of vitality, and sometimes violence. They liken it to the blare of conches, and to it they attribute passions and rages. This is extraordinary, for an experiment on colour and sound was carried out by a Frenchman in 1834. He asked a blind man what he thought red was like, and the man said it must be like the sound of trumpets. He then asked a deaf man what he imagined would be the sound of trumpets, and the man wrote, " Like the colour red."

Some years ago the French firm of MM Lumiere, photographic plate makers of Lyons, noticed that workers in dark rooms lit by red lamps soon became quarrelsome and bad tempered. So the dark rooms were lit with green lamps, and the men were calm, good tempered and noticeably fresher at the end of the day. This is in keeping with the yoga theory that green is a harmonious, peaceful colour, soothing, but not sad. Blue, they said, was cool and tranquil; violet was melancholy; and purple impressive, stately and royal. White has always been the colour of innocence and rejoicing among the Hindus. It is worn both at weddings and funerals, for despite outward manifestations of sorrow, death is to them a release into a better, happier world.

Many famous musicians and artists have compared sound with colour, and in a surprising number of instances, the results have tallied. What is more surprising still is that they have tallied with the corresponding sounds and colours which the yogis said were related. Van Gogh was so certain that colour and sound were related that he took piano lessons to improve his colour sense. The lessons were discontinued only when he persisted in comparing the various notes to Prussian blue, sepia, emerald green, chrome yellow and cobalt, and his instructor felt that he was dealing with a maniac. And was it not Arthur Rimbaud who invited his sweetheart to ride in a cab " as green as the music of an oboe ? "

The first European to associate colour with music scientifically was the Jesuit, Father Castel, who invented the ocular keyboard, so that the colours of the prism were harnessed to notes: C to blue, C sharp to willow green, D to light green, D sharp to olive green, E to yellow, F to saffron, F sharp to orange, G to red, G sharp to crimson, A to violet, A sharp to violet-blue.

Later, an English clergyman, the Rev. William Guthrie, maintained that colours had individual properties; that red was warm and passionate, blue cold and solemn, green was conducive to meditation, yellow produced joy, and brown sadness. He preached in a church illuminated by coloured lights, the colours changing according to his mood and the force of his utterances. His methods gained him huge audiences but were not popular with the clergy who said that they made preaching even more theatrical than it was.

Abbe Polycarpe Poncelet, a contemporary of Father Castel went so far as to suggest that there was an affinity between taste and music; that acid flavours corresponded to C; sweet flavours to E; and " that a lemon with sugar is a simple but charming consonance in the fifth major."

Let us dismiss none of these theories as claptrap. There is a substratum of truth in them all. Did not Beethoven call B minor the black key, and did not Schubert say, " As E minor has naturally one colour, the tonality may be likened unto a maiden robed in white with a rose-red bow on her breast ? " Liszt, too, when he was *Kappellmeister* at Weimar used to say to his orchestra, " Gentlemen, not so much black. This last time it has been too much black." They understood.

The idea of the colour organ was first thought of by Alexander Scriabine, who experimented with Dr. Myers, the psychologist, in order to perfect one. After hundreds of tests they decided that C major is red, D major orange, A major yellow, B major blue, F sharp major violet. They started with red C major and rose roughly by fifths, so that the order in which the notes and colours were arranged suggested a spectrum from red to violet.

The odd thing about all this is that though people may agree about the effects of sound and colour, they disagree about the sounds they hear and the colours they see; for our hearing and sight are so insensitive that no two people see or hear exactly the same thing or sound. Colour blindness is caused by the inability of the eye to respond to certain portions of the spectrum. Scriabine discovered this when he met Rimsky-Korsakoff at a concert in Paris. " A very golden key," commented Rimsky-Korsakoff of a piece that was D major. Scriabine agreed. Later, in the course of conversation Scriabine expressed his fondness for the key of F sharp major, adding, " I like violet overtones."

" Violet ! " Rimsky-Korsakoff thundered; " are you blind ? Why, the key of F-sharp major is bright green ! "

Colour science is an infant science. The yogis started it and progressed well along the road. Red was their most primitive colour. They warned their disciples against its power. Never sleep, they warned, in a room that is painted red. Centuries later Dr. Donald Laird of Colgate University made thousands of experiments with sleep and colour, and proved that if red predominates in the colour scheme of a bedroom, it is likely to keep people awake, even in the dark !

The normal person cannot see beyond the forty ninth octave of vibrations, which is the limit of the visible spectrum, but there are some so sensitive that they can pierce the veil in the ultra-violet direction, into the etheric. Those who do not possess this extra-sensitivity can do so through chemically treated glass screens, and Dr. Kilner, once of the pioneers in this work, states that every person has an aura, luminous and often multi-coloured, and that auras differ, though the average is blue-green. Those possessed of excessive vitality have red auras; intellectuals, yellow.

Another scientist, Deighton Patmore, says that roughly speaking, humanity is divided into three groups; the intuitive, imaginative type possesses a orange-red aura;

the brain worker has a yellow aura; and the normal man blue-green.

Dr. Alexander Cannon, a scientist who has also practised yoga for years, says that colour affects the glands; that red stimulates, purple heals, orange brightens, blue soothes, green pleases, and brown rests. Colours have a subtle power, and the yogis tell us that we should use them to make our lives healthier, happier and fuller; that our homes—if not our surroundings—should be so harmonious that we shall want to return to them, and there live in peace with our families.

How many homes are like that? In how many homes are the colours so discordant or ugly that they frighten, depress or irritate one; where the radio blares from morning till night, whether people listen to it or not, till one is compelled to flee, shrieking, from the place?

Everyone can paint a room or a home to make it look cheerful and pleasant; we can use gramophone or radio music in the same way, or shut it off. The vibrant yoga sounds can be used in conjunction with breathing. The simpler *mantras* can be repeated silently at various times of the day to calm the mind. But the awakening of *kundalini* or the attainment of *Siddhi* are possible only if many hours each day are spent in yoga practices. They are not possible for a person with an eight-hour job and a limited amount of leisure.

CHAPTER X

Electricity—the source of Life

YOGA is not a religion. It does not matter what religious belief you subscribe to, you can be a yogi and follow yoga ideas and practices without offence. Yoga strives after absolute truth, which as all seekers know, is as easy to capture as a sunbeam in a dark cellar.

Unlike the followers of many religions, yogis refuse to be satisfied with comfortable beliefs, either about the origin of Man or his ultimate destination. They have tried, with about as much success as modern scientists, to discover what life is; what it is that makes us tick, and where that life force goes when we die.

They have never found a completely satisfactory answer to these questions. Some yogis are able—so they affirm—to continue living indefinitely, but when they have reached the limit of development possible on earth, they will prepare themselves for death and the release of *purusha*, or the soul.

They reject the idea of a Creator, but say that all matter is created out of some central force called *Prakriti*. *Prakriti* is what we call Nature. Throughout yogic writings we see references to *akasha* or *akasa* (ether) and the *rajas* (energy). They speak of energy flowing through the *nadis* and infusing the body with life and energy. One cannot escape the feeling that they hit upon the identical truth that scientists have discovered within recent years; that the basis of life is electricity.

We know that sensations are conveyed to the brain along tiny nerve fibres, and that when they reach the brain certain electrical impulses are set up by means of which messages are sent to the limbs, which set them in motion.

In the past Europeans believed that the seat of the emotions was at various times the stomach and the heart. But centuries ago the yogis considered the cerebrum as *brahma chakra*, the very centre of thought, and they said that *akasha* travelled along the subarahnoid cavity. The channel along which this force reached the *brahma chakra* was the spinal cord or *shushumna nadi*, and its power was radiated to the various glands. Many of their *asanas* were devised specifically for gland development.

Broadly speaking this is what we find today. As related earlier, thoughts travel along the nerve centres, most of which are attached to the spinal cord, to the brain, and when emotions are set up they cause the glands to secrete certain substances in the bloodstream; and these affect our entire being.

The yogis say that thoughts are material things. Scientists are not certain about this, but accept the possibility. By 'material things' we mean energy in a form so minute that it cannot be seen even under the most powerful microscope. This is feasible, for today scientists are dealing with matter that is incredibly minute. A scientific paper I was reading not long ago tells me that the diameter of an electron is 3/20,000,000,-

000,000 of an inch; that the diameter of a proton is 1/25,000,000,000,000 of an inch, and that protons travel at a speed of 540,000,000 miles an hour ! A proton is so heavy that if a billiard ball were made of closely packed protons it would weigh millions of tons.

It is possible that either thought, or electrical energy, which may be forms of the same thing, are composed of these very minute *material* particles. When used like this the word material ceases to have its normal meaning.

Dr. Gilbert Ryle, Professor of Metaphysicial Philosophy at Oxford, says, " In ordinary life (save when we want to sound knowing) we seldom use the word ' mind ' or the adjective ' mental ' at all. What we do is to talk about people calculating, conjuring, hoping, resolving, tasting, bluffing, fretting and so on. Nor in ordinary life do we talk of ' matter ' or of things being ' material.' What we do is to talk of steel, granite and water; or of wood, moss and grain; of flesh, bone and sinew. The umbrella-titles ' mind ' and ' matter ' obliterate the very differences that ought to interest us. Theorists should drop both these words. ' Mind ' and ' matter ' are echoes from the hustings of philosophy and prejudice the solutions of all problems posed in terms of them."

The unscientific speak of yoga being a conquest of mind over matter. It is nothing of the sort. They are not different things, but different forms of the same thing. Injure certain portions of the brain (matter), and what happens to the mind ? The interaction of what we term mind and matter is so complete, and interference with one affects the other so violently, that we can conclude, as the yogis did, that they are the same thing. Poison a man or injure his head, and then what happens to his mind ? Does it continue to function independently ?

The yogis say that the seat of the soul—that something which makes us tick and leaves us when we die—is situated in the pineal gland. Not long ago Dr. James W. Papez, Professor of Anatomy at Cornell University, stated that the emotions and consciousness originate in a ring-shaped structure situated deep in the middle of the brain. This, he stated, was called the seat of the soul by the ancient Hindus. It is composed of four somewhat puzzling sections of the brain which act as central stations for receiving and sending messages to and from the body and the higher brain centre, and it is this that makes Man so different from the lower animals.

We are groping today, just as the yogis did centuries ago, for a link between the mechanical processes of the brain and the actual machinery of thought. Some years ago a research worker at St. Thomas' Hospital, London, declared that he actually saw thought waves. These, recorded on a sensitizer invented by him, were three hundred millionths of a millimetre in length. "When I have fully established their existence," he said, "I shall have brought transmission of thought from a possibility to a scientific probability." Incidentally, waves of that length are the same length as the shortest rays that reach us from the sun, so it may be that all thought, all electricity, all energy on this earth comes from solar radiation.

What was the original source of such energy? Who can say in a universe consisting of a globe of ether with a circumference so vast that if we travelled at 186,000 miles a second it would take us—if time stood still, for the universe is expanding, about 500,000,000,000 years to circumnavigate it?

In the theory put forward by Bondi and Gold, of Cambridge University, and endorsed by Hoyle, the universe is expanding so rapidly that all the galaxies now visible will be beyond the limit of our vision in 10,000 million years because they will be moving away from us faster than the speed of light, which comes from them to us.

From time to time we read of robots and mechanical brains, machines which work out prodigious sums in a matters of seconds; calculations that would take a team of scientists ten or twenty years. All such calculating machines work on the same principle as the mechanism of the brain. We know what happens when electrical impulses are passed to the brain, and we know the definite reactions that follow. But we don't know why. Once we know this, we can invent a mechanical robot that will think and reason for itself, and we shall be well on the road to solving the secret of life itself.

The heart is an electrical generator. In some way the yogis hit upon this. They did not use the term ' electrical ' but merely called it ' life force.' And they realized that breathing has a close connection with the beating of the heart, and if breathing could be controlled, the action of the heart, too, could be controlled, and by mastering the art of breathing, life could be continued almost indefinitely.

Without knowing it they were centuries ahead of their time. That, perhaps, is why their philosophy had to be watered down, corrupted to suit the masses. In 1856 a European scientist first detected heart waves. In 1903 the Leyden physiologist, William Einthoven, devised an instrument to pick up and record the electrical currents generated by the heart. The electrocardiograph is a development of this. By means of this instrument the expert can tell whether the four chambers of the heart are synchronising, and if not, exactly which of them is faulty.

Recently Dr. Frederick Lemere, of Seattle, was called in by an insurance company to test a blind workman who claimed compensation because he was blinded by the shortcircuiting of a live wire in the workroom. Electrodes were attached to his head, and slow alpha waves, characteristic of the brain in darkness, were recorded. He was awarded full compensation.

The brain of a woman, blinded by a fugue or brainstorm, produced waves of a different type, so Dr. Lemere assured her that with treatment she would be able to see, and ultimately her sight was restored.

In a recent broadcast Dr. E. T. O. Slater, Physician in Psychiatric Medicine to the National Hospital, London, said that hunger and fatigue impaired consciousness in a human being because his stocks of food—especially sugar, which gives energy—were running low, and when blood sugar ran low, electrical changes took place in the surface of the brain. Normally a recording of these waves reads from 8 to 10 cycles a second, but when the concentration of sugar in the blood is lowered, this rate drops to 5 or 6 cycles There is therefore, a definite relation between a change in the chemistry of the blood, a change in electrical activity of the brain, and a change in consciousness.

The food we eat, the work we perform, the environment we live in, the air we breathe and the way we breathe it, and the thoughts we think, all have some

151

effect on the blood. This either accelerates or slows down the wave cycles of the brain and affects our thought processes. Thus, everything we do or think, affects our lives. Once again science and yoga agree.

In certain types of yoga breathing so much carbonic acid gas is washed out of the blood that for a space we feel dizzy. This merely means that the rate of electrical waves has increased, and consciousness is more acute, and it is this sensitivity that one constantly strives after in yoga. The more sensitive the brain, the more receptive are we to external influences, and the better able to draw upon the illimitable resources of Nature.

We are as yet on the brink of virgin territory, for the brain is still largely uncharted. The body, too has its electrical responses and a great deal of work has been done on the subject both in Europe and America to show that fit organs and limbs have different electrical resistances from those that are diseased. Dr. E. N. Goodman, of the Columbia College of Physicians and Surgeons, found that the electrical potential of the stomach varies when empty and full; in sickness and in health. Dr. Goodman, Dr. Richter of John Hopkins Hospital, Baltimore, and others have developed this form of diagnosis, and in the near future all hospitals and clinics will be equipped with electrical recording machines that will render diagnosis a much more accurate affair than it is today.

There is an astounding similarity between all living things; men, beasts, trees and plants. And when we probe a little further, we shall find that the similarity extends also to mineral matter.

A tree needs oxygen just as a man or a dog. In the tree, the chemical changes which take place are surprisingly like those that take place in the body. Roots must have oxygen, just as a man or a dog; and oxygen is used in much the same sort of chemical process. Normally, oxygen does not combine with sugar unless heated; but in all living things it does so through enzymes.

In 1924 a scientist named Warburg discovered that the oxygen we breathe unites with an enzyme that is mainly protein and in 1926 J. B. S. Haldane found by experiment that the same thing happens with green plants, moths and rats!

All living creatures utilize oxygen in the same way. From here let us take a further stride. Sir William Bragg, the eminent physicist, once said, "Electricity is the way matter behaves." But years have passed since he made that statement and other scientists have added that electricity is not only the way matter behaves; but it *is* matter!

The chemicals which comprise the body—carbon, iron, nitrogen, oxygen, phosphorus, etc.—combine to form a perfect electric battery, and the food we eat enables it to discharge itself.

Death is usually caused by disintegration of the cells of the plate due to faulty feeding or bad living. Charge a man, a dog or a tree with the wrong food, and sooner or later you will destroy that energy which makes them move or think.

The yogis claim that by living out of doors, in contact with Nature, a man can replenish his reserves of energy. If electricity be that energy, he certainly can, for the very particles of moisture in the atmosphere are charged with minute quantities of static electricity; trees and plants such as rice and clover get their stores of nitrogen from lightning flashes, and all moving water, such as waterfalls, rivers and seas, throws out minute charges of electricity. The earth, too, is a vast electrical reservoir, for current, when released, finds its way into the earth. That is why health is improved if the body has contact with the earth; walking on dewy grass, or sleeping outdoors on new mown hay. The yogis say that in some mysterious way power enters and restores energy. They said this long before the cults of nudism, hiking and camping.

Dr. Alexis Carrel, who long tried to probe the secret of life, said that the cells of the human body are in themselves immortal, and death is the price we pay for brains. " It is only because the cells are subject to a mysterious energy released by the brain, that they die." That waste of energy is caused by high blood pressure, the hardening of the arteries, cancer, stomach ulcers and other diseases, caused by worry, anxiety, fear, hatred, envy and the many emotions which the fretful minds of men conjure up for their own destruction.

The only way to stop this electrical discharge and subsequent decay of the body is by bringing metabolism to a halt. Professor de Lampl, of Leyden, came near to the solution when he studied the remains of animals that had died in Siberia and the Polar regions, and which after centuries were still in a state of perfect preservation.

Professor de Lampl actually prepared a hormone from the extract of young cows, which, in the course of an experiment he injected into the bloodstream of a Miss Anna Broogg. Miss Broogg's body had degenerated rapidly, till at 30 she looked well over fifty.

Professor Lampl made her fast for 48 hours; then gave her an anaesthetic. He injected the serum and placed her in a freezing tunnel where she lay for 42 days, during which period metabolism was completely suspended.

After the experiment a group of doctors examined Anna Broogg, who stated that the 42 days had passed as rapidly as a single night. She looked and felt like a girl aged twenty !

Dr. Carrel said: " I believe that it will soon be possible to put people into a state of suspended animation for long periods, and if they are willing to undergo this treatment periodically, they will live for centuries.

This is exactly what the yogis do. They journey to the Himalayas or some quiet spot, prepare themselves and fall into a trance, suspend all animation and thoroughly rest and recharge their burnt out batteries. Then after days or weeks they allow themselves to be revived, and by this means defy the ravages of time.

The body is some form of electrical battery. In it are the chemicals we eat, drink and breathe. By means of some mysterious alchemy as yet unfathomed, these chemicals manufacture the electric current that replenishes the battery. Only by wrong thinking and faulty living do we destroy the means of re-generation and so commit suicide.

Yoga theory is that life is produced by some external force—call it what you wish—God, electricity, ether, soul or some convenient term. Drs. H. S. Burr and F. S. C. Northopp, of Yale, say that electricity is the cause of life. They have conducted thousands of experiments, many on eggs, and have found electrical fields in the most elementary forms of embryo. Electricity is a form of matter, a theory borne out by the fact that if a great quantity of current (amperes) is sent through a wire, it meets with resistance; and if a great number of amperes is sent through the same wire, the resistance will be so great that it becomes red hot and melts.

Christians regard the soul as a part of the body that lives on after death. In our minds we think of the here-after as being ' a place ' where the soul will continue to enjoy the things we enjoy here; peach Melbas, mush-room omelettes, and old brandy. The soul, too, will presumably love the smell of freshly roasted coffee, a good cigar and the scent of new mown hay. Such are the limitations of most minds that we cannot imagine a state after death, that will differ in essentials from life. We hope to be tickled by a cartoon in the comic papers, or a good play; to take pleasure in a crackling log fire on a bitter day, or a glass of iced shandy on a hot one. Presumably Englishmen will have English souls that crave for bacon, eggs and marmalade for breakfast; and Chinese souls will hanker after sharks' fins and birds' nest soup. Most women must imagine heaven as a place hung with Paris frocks. We can't imagine a good time without the ingredients of a good time here. It would indeed, be a grim outlook for most of us if we felt that our souls will merely zoom through damp clouds till eternity.

The yogis do not use the term ' soul ' in the sense of a nebulous, disembodied entity floating aimlessly about the ether after death. They believe in, and make prac-tical provision for the passing on of their bodies from one generation to another, by the normal process of generation. They hope that their ancestors will, by the noble and generous inheritance they have received, prove to be better and nobler examples of the race than they were.

In this sense only, do they believe in reincarnation. There is nothing in genuine yoga writings which leads one to assume any other theory of reincarnation, except that of gradual evolution. This, too, is in step with scientific thought. It can be achieved only by the way we live, by the deeds we perform, and the thoughts we think.

Yoga philosophy is so complete that it has stood the test of centuries. Each day the disciples of yoga grow in number.

BIBLIOGRAPHY

Yoga for You	*Claude Bragdon*
14 Lessons in Yogi Philosophy	*Ramacharaka*
The Yoga Sutras of Patanjali	*Chas Johnston*
The Wisdom of the Overself	*Paul Brunton*
The Secret Path	*Paul Brunton*
A Search of Secret India	*Paul Brunton*
Tantrik Yoga: Hindu and Tibetan	*J. Marquis-Riviere*
Inner Teaching and Yoga	*Chas Wase*
Extra-Sensory Perception	*J. B. Rhine*
Yoga	*K. T. Behanan*
Yogic Home Exercises	*Swami Sivananda*
Yoga—Personal Hygiene	*Shri Yogendra*
Yoga and the Science of Health	*Felix Guyot*
Yoga for the West	*Felix Guyot*
Yoga Explained	*F. Yeats-Brown*
Lancer at Large	*F. Yeats-Brown*
Science of Breath	*Ramacharaka*
Gland Treatment	*Grace Sturat*
Heaven Lies Within Us	*Theos Bernard*
The Yoga System of Health	*Yogi Vithaldas*
Yogic Asanas	*V. G. Rele*
The Mysterious Kundalini	*V. G. Rele*
Tibetan and Yoga Secret Doctrines	*W. Y. Evans-Wentz*
Wisdom from the East	*Hari Prasad Shastru*
Yoga and Western Psychology	*Gwendoline Coster*
Goraknath and the Kanpatha Yogis	*G. W. Briggs*
My Journey to Lhassa	*Alexandra David-Neel*
With Mystics and Magicians in Tibet	*Alexandra David-Neel*
The Invisible Influence	*Alexandra Cannon*
Hypnotism	*Alexandra Cannon*
Raja Yoga or Occultism	*H. P. Blavatsky*
Yoga Aphorisms of Patanjali	*Rajendralala Mitra*
Religion of the Veda	*M. Bloomfield*
Religion of the Rig-Veda	*H. D. Griswold*
The Samkaya System	*A. B. Keith*
The Philosophy of the Upanishads	*P. Deussen*
Autobiography of a Yogi	*Yogananda (Swami)*

INDEX

INDEX